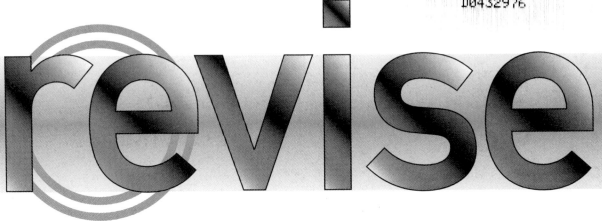

GCSE
Biology

David Applin

with Tony Buzan

Hodder & Stoughton

A MEMBER OF THE HODDER HEADLINE GROUP

Key to symbols

As you read through this book you will notice the following symbols. They will help you find your way around the book more quickly.

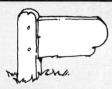 points you to other parts of the book where related topics are explained

 shows a handy hint to help you remember something

 shows you a short list of key facts

 shows a sequence of linked processes

 means remember!!!

 refers you from a diagram to a checklist of related points

 says Did you know this? – interesting points to note

Acknowledgements

Copyright photographs have been used, with permission, from the following sources: Planet Earth Pictures (p.23); Science Photo Library (pp. 38, 117)

ISBN 0 340 66391 X

First published 1997
Impression number   10 9 8 7 6 5 4 3 2 1
Year   2001 2000 1999 1998 1997

The 'Teach Yourself' name and logo are registered trade marks of Hodder & Stoughton Ltd.

Designed and produced by Gecko Ltd, Bicester, Oxon
Printed in Great Britain for Hodder & Stoughton Educational, a division of Hodder Headline Plc, 338 Euston Road, London NW1 3BH by Scotprint Ltd, Musselburgh, Scotland.

Mind Maps: Patrick Mayfield, Gareth Morris, Vanda North
Illustrations: Peter Bull, Simon Cooke, Chris Etheridge, Ian Law, Joe Little, Andrea Norton, Mike Parsons, John Plumb, Dave Poole, Chris Rothero, Anthony Warne
Cover design: Amanda Hawkes
Cover illustration: Paul Bateman

Contents

Revision made easy

The four pages that follow contain a gold mine of information on how you can achieve success both at school and in your exams. Read them and apply the information, and you will be able to spend less, but more efficient, time studying, with better results. If you already have another *Hodder & Stoughton Revision Guide*, skim-read these pages to remind yourself about the exciting new techniques the books use, then move ahead to page 8.

This section gives you vital information on how to remember more *while* you are learning and how to remember more *after* you have finished studying. It explains

> **how to use special techniques to improve your memory**

> **how to use a revolutionary note-taking technique called Mind Maps that will double your memory and help you to write essays and answer exam questions**

> **how to read everything faster while at the same time improving your comprehension and concentration**

All this information is packed into the next four pages, so make sure you read them!

Your *amazing* memory

There are five important things you must know about your brain and memory to revolutionise your school life.

1 **how your memory ('recall') works *while* you are learning**

2 **how your memory works *after* you have finished learning**

3 **how to use Mind Maps – a special technique for helping you with all aspects of your studies**

4 **how to increase your reading speed**

5 **how to zap your revision**

1 Recall during learning – the need for breaks

When you are studying, your memory can concentrate, understand and remember well for between 20 and 45 minutes at a time. Then it *needs* a break. If you carry on for longer than this without one, your memory starts to break down! If you study for hours non-stop, you will remember only a fraction of what you have been trying to learn, and you will have wasted valuable revision time.

So, ideally, *study for less than an hour*, then take a five- to ten-minute break. During the break listen to music, go for a walk, do some exercise, or just daydream. (Daydreaming is a necessary brain-power booster – geniuses do it regularly.) During the break your brain will be sorting out what it has been learning, and you will go back to your books with the new information safely stored and organised in your memory banks. We recommend breaks at regular intervals as you work through the *Revision Guides*. Make sure you take them!

2 Recall after learning – the waves of your memory

What do you think begins to happen to your memory straight *after* you have finished learning something? Does it immediately start forgetting? No! Your brain actually *increases* its power and carries on remembering. For a short time after your study session, your brain integrates the information, making a more complete picture of everything it has just learnt. Only then does the rapid decline in memory begin, and as much as 80 per cent of what you have learnt can be forgotten in a day.

However, if you catch the top of the wave of your memory, and briefly review (look back over) what you have been revising at the correct time, the memory is stamped in far more strongly, and stays at the crest of the wave for a much longer time. To maximise your brain's power to remember, take a few minutes and use a Mind Map to review what you have learnt at the end of a day. Then review it at the end of a week, again at the end of a month, and finally a week before the exams. That way you'll ride your memory wave all the way to your exam – and beyond!

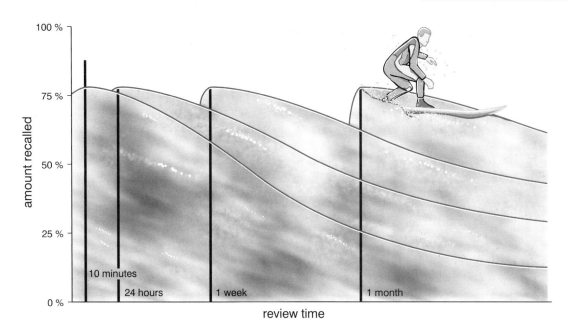

Amazing as your memory is (think of everything you actually do have stored in your brain at this moment) the principles on which it operates are very simple: your brain will remember if it (a) has an image (a picture or a symbol); (b) has that image fixed and (c) can link that image to something else.

3 The Mind Map® – a picture of the way you think

Do you *like* taking notes? More importantly, do you like having to go back over and learn them before exams? Most students I know certainly do not! And how do you take your notes? Most people take notes on lined paper, using blue or black ink. The result, visually, is *boring*! And what does your brain do when it is bored? It turns off, tunes out, and goes to sleep! Add a dash of colour, rhythm, imagination, and the whole note-taking process becomes much more fun, uses more of your brain's abilities, *and* improves your recall and understanding.

A Mind Map mirrors the way your brain works. It can be used for note-taking from books or in class, for reviewing what you have just studied, for revising, and for essay planning for coursework and in exams. It uses all your memory's natural techniques to build up your rapidly growing 'memory muscle'.

You will find Mind Maps throughout this book. Study them, add some colour, personalise them, and then have a go at drawing your own – you'll remember them far better! Put them on your walls and in your files for a quick-and-easy review of the topic.

How to draw a Mind Map

❶ Start in the middle of the page with the page turned sideways. This gives your brain the maximum room for its thoughts.

❷ Always start by drawing a small picture or symbol. Why? Because a picture is worth a thousand words to your brain. And try to use at least three colours, as colour helps your memory even more.

❸ Let your thoughts flow, and write or draw your ideas on coloured branching lines connected to your central image. These key symbols and words are the headings for your topic. The Mind Map at the top of the next page shows you how to start.

❹ Then add facts and ideas by drawing more, smaller, branches on to the appropriate main branches, just like a tree.

❺ Always print your word clearly on its line. Use only one word per line. The Mind Map at the foot of the

next page shows you how to do this.

❻ To link ideas and thoughts on different branches, use arrows, colours, underlining, and boxes.

How to read a Mind Map

❶ Begin in the centre, the focus of your topic.

❷ The words/images attached to the centre are like chapter headings, read them next.

❸ Always read out from the centre, in every direction (even on the left-hand side, where you will have to read from right to left, instead of the usual left to right).

Using Mind Maps

Mind Maps are a versatile tool – use them for taking notes in class or from books, for solving problems, for brainstorming with friends, and for reviewing and revising for exams – their uses are endless! You will find them invaluable for planning essays for coursework and exams. Number your main branches in the order in which you want to use them and off you go – the main headings for your essay are done and all your ideas are logically organised!

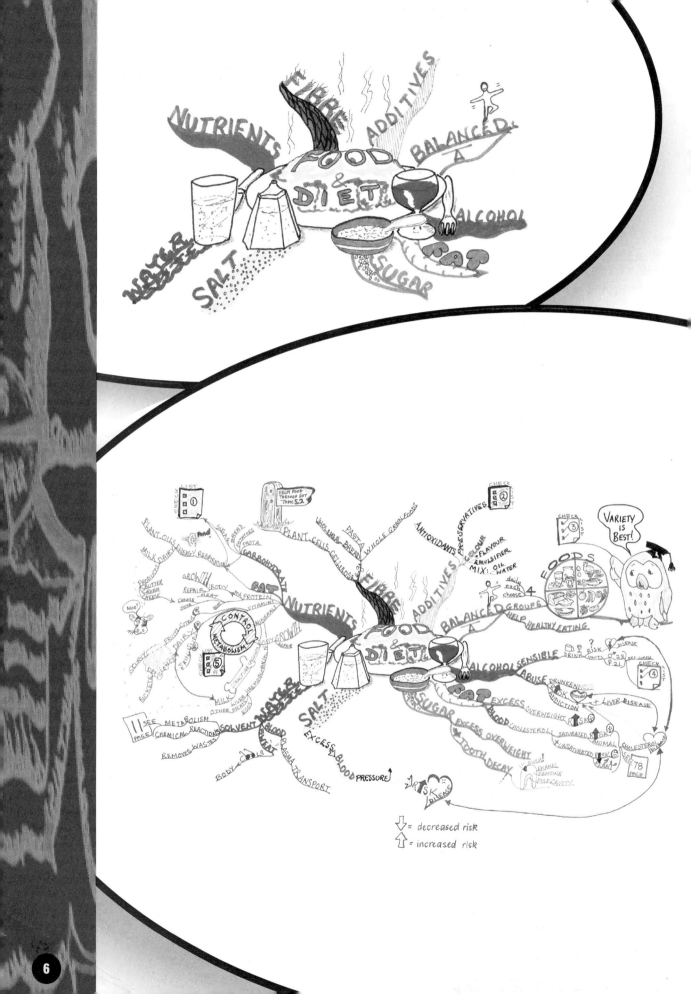

⬇ = decreased risk
⬆ = increased risk

4 Super speed reading

It seems incredible, but it's been proved – the faster you read, the more you understand and remember! So here are some tips to help you to practise reading faster – you'll cover the ground more quickly, remember more, *and* have more time for revision!

★ First read the whole text (whether it's a lengthy book or an exam paper) very quickly, to give your brain an overall idea of what's ahead and get it working. (It's like sending out a scout to look at the territory you have to cover – it's much easier when you know what to expect!) Then read the text again for more detailed information.

★ Have the text a reasonable distance away from your eyes. In this way your eye/brain system will be able to see more at a glance, and will naturally begin to read faster.

★ Take in groups of words at a time. Rather than reading 'slowly and carefully' read faster, more enthusiastically. Your comprehension will rocket!

★ Take in phrases rather than single words while you read.

★ Use a guide. Your eyes are designed to follow movement, so a thin pencil underneath the lines you are reading, moved smoothly along, will 'pull' your eyes to faster speeds.

5 Helpful hints for exam revision

Start to revise at the beginning of the course. Cram at the start, not the end and avoid 'exam panic'!

Use Mind Maps throughout your course, and build a Master Mind Map for each subject – a giant Mind Map that summarises everything you know about the subject.

Use memory techniques such as mnemonics (verses or systems for remembering things like dates and events, or lists).

Get together with one or two friends to revise, compare Mind Maps, and discuss topics.

And finally...

★ *Have fun while you learn* – studies show that those people who enjoy what they are doing understand and remember it more, and generally do it better.

★ *Use your teachers* as resource centres. Ask them for help with specific topics and with more general advice on how you can improve your all-round performance.

★ *Personalise your Revision Guide* by underlining and highlighting, by adding notes and pictures. Allow your brain to have a conversation with it!

Your brain is an amazing piece of equipment – learn to use it, and you, like thousands of students before you will be able to master 'B's and 'A's with ease. The more you understand and use your brain, the more it will repay you!

GCSE *Biology* and this Revision Guide

How to use this book

This Revision Guide is not intended to replace your textbooks. As tests and examinations approach, however, many students feel the need to revise from something a good deal shorter than their usual textbook. This Revision Guide is intended to fill that need. It covers all the GCSE Biology syllabuses for the different Examining Groups.

To use the book most effectively, make sure that you read Tony Buzan's notes on 'Revision made easy'. Draw a Mind Map of each topic as you work through the book. Make a timetable for revision, using the contents list on page 3 to ensure that you cover all of the topics on your syllabus. Planned use of time and concentrated study will give you time for other activities and interests as well as work.

Each revision topic begins with a set of Test Yourself questions to give you an idea of how well you have already grasped the topic. There is a set of Round-up questions at the end of each topic. Work out your Improvement Index from your score on the Round-up questions compared with your score on the Test Yourself questions.

When the exam arrives

When the exam arrives, you should have confidence if you have revised thoroughly. In the examination room, attempt all the questions you are supposed to answer and make sure that you turn over every page. Many marks have been lost in exams as a result of turning over two pages at once. If you suffer a panic attack, breathe deeply and slowly to get lots of oxygen into your system and clear your thoughts. Your examination is important, but above all, keep it in perspective.

A note on content

Part of the content of GCSE Science: Biology is specified by the National Curriculum. This part of the content is required by all the Examining Groups. The rest of the content is extension material chosen by the Examining Groups and there are differences between their syllabuses. Each Examining Group requires some topics but not others. However, a number of topics (e.g. aspects of health and disease) are part of the syllabuses of the majority of Examining Groups. Carefully check the syllabus of the Examining Group you are following to find out which extension material you need to revise in this *Biology Revision Guide*.

I wish you success.

David Applin

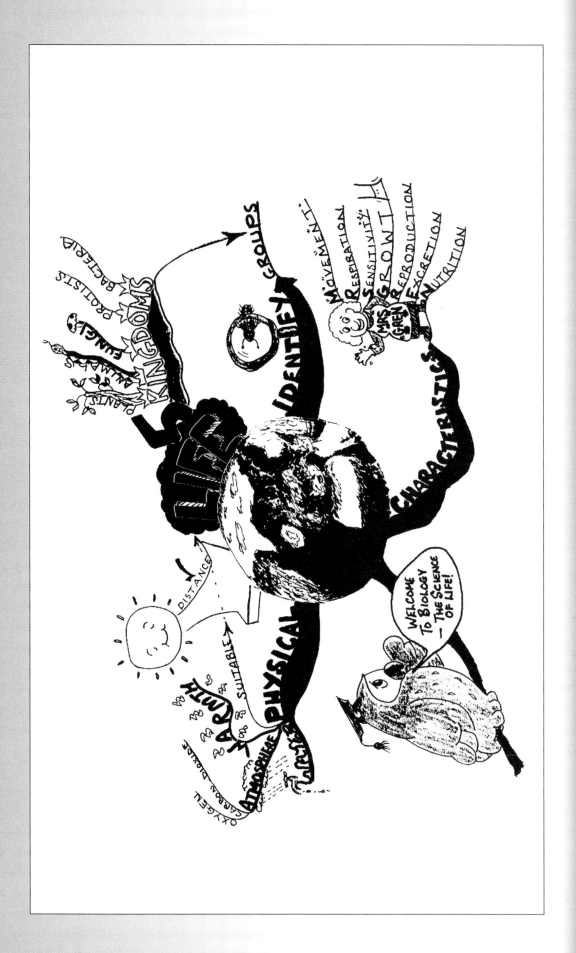

Introducing biology

How much do you already know?
Work out your score on page 133.

Test yourself

1 What would happen to the ground temperature if Earth were **a)** nearer to the Sun **b)** further from the Sun? [2]

2 a) List the processes which tell you that something is living. [$7 \times \frac{1}{2}$]

b) Put a tick (✓) next to the processes which you think apply to animals. [$7 \times \frac{1}{2}$]

c) Put a cross (✗) next to the processes which you think apply to plants. [$6 \times \frac{1}{2}$]

d) Do plants and animals have the same characteristics? If not, how are they different? [1]

3 Using the forget-me-not and oak tree as examples, explain the meaning of the words 'annual' and 'perennial'. [3]

4 a) What is a biological key used for? [1]

b) Why are features like exact colour, size and mass not suitable for including in a biological key? [3]

5 List the physical features of soil which make it a suitable place for earthworms to live. [4]

1.1 Living on Earth

preview

At the end of this section you will:
- **understand why Earth is a suitable place for living things (organisms)**
- **know that soil, air and water are the physical environments in which organisms live.**

Why the Earth can support life

Earth is a planet in orbit round a star we call the Sun. It is the only planet we know of that supports life.

★ Earth is close enough to the Sun for its surface temperature to be in the range in which life can exist. The temperature at the Earth's surface varies between −70 and 55°C.

★ Earth is massive enough to have sufficient gravity to hold down an atmosphere of different gases essential for living organisms.

★ The layer of ozone which surrounds Earth reduces the amount of ultraviolet light from the Sun reaching the planet's surface. Too much ultraviolet light destroys living things.

Limits on life

9000 m limit for springtails (tiny insects) which feed on pollen and seeds blown up by the wind

Mount Everest – highest mountain

10 000

permanent snow

5000

tree line

soil forms a thin layer covering most of the Earth's land surface

air forms an atmosphere of gases around the Earth

6000 m limit for flowering plants

metres 0

sea level

light – photosynthesis possible

biosphere – the places on Earth where there is life

4500 m limit for farming

5000

100 m deep limit for plant-like phytoplankton

10 000

Mariana Trench – deepest part of the ocean

15 000

water (fresh and salt) covers 75% of the Earth's surface

Ocean depths – no light. Life here depends on falling dead organisms, and thermal and chemical energy from deep sea vents.

Earth's physical environment

The diagram on the opposite page shows that soil, air and water form Earth's environment:

★ **Soil** is formed when the weather, the roots of plants and the different activities of animals break down rocks into small particles.

★ **Air** consists of: 78% nitrogen; 21% oxygen; 0.03% carbon dioxide; and less than 1% water vapour, argon, xenon and other gases.

★ **Water** fills the seas, oceans, rivers and lakes. About 2% of the Earth's water is locked up as ice, in the soil, in the bodies of living things or is vapour in the atmosphere.

1.2 Characteristics of life

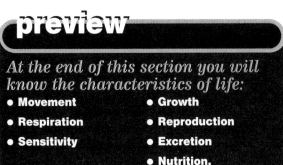

At the end of this section you will know the characteristics of life:
- Movement
- Respiration
- Sensitivity
- Growth
- Reproduction
- Excretion
- Nutrition.

Handy hint

The mnemonic **Mrs Gren** will help you remember the characteristics of living things.

More about MRS GREN

The characteristics of life are the features that are common to all living things:

★ **Movement**: animals are able to move from place to place because of the action of **muscles** which pull on the **skeleton**. Plants do not usually move from place to place; they move mainly by **growing**.

★ **Respiration** occurs in cells, and releases energy from food for life's activities. **Aerobic** respiration uses oxygen to release energy from food. **Anaerobic** respiration releases energy from food without using oxygen.

★ **Sensitivity** allows living things to detect changes in their surroundings and respond to them.

★ **Growth** leads to an increase in size. **Development** occurs as young change and become adult in appearance.

★ **Reproduction** produces new individuals.

★ **Excretion** removes the waste substances produced by the chemical reactions (called **metabolism**) taking place in cells.

★ **Nutrition** makes food (by the process of photosynthesis) or takes in food for use in the body.

Remember
- **Respiration** releases energy from food.
- **Gaseous exchange** takes in oxygen for respiration and removes carbon dioxide produced by respiration.
- **Excretion** removes wastes produced by metabolism.
- **Defecation** (or egestion) removes the undigested remains of food.

1.3 Grouping living things

preview

At the end of this section you will:
- **understand that groups of living things are named according to Linnaeus' system of classification**
- **know the major groups of plants and animals**
- **understand binomial names.**

Classification

Living things which have features in common are grouped together. Organising living things into groups is called **classification**. Some characteristics are unique to the group; other characteristics are shared with other groups. Groups therefore combine to form larger groups. The largest group of all is the **kingdom**. Each:

- kingdom contains a number of **phyla**
- phyl**um** (singular) contains a number of **classes**
- class contains a number of **orders**
- order contains a number of **families**
- family contains a number of **genera**
- gen**us** (singular) contains one or more **species**.

Arachnids
- The body is made up of two parts.
- There are 8 legs.
- Scorpions, mites and harvestmen are close relatives of spiders.

Cnidarians
- The body has no front or rear. Its parts are arranged evenly in the round.
- Tentacles surround an opening which is both mouth and anus.
- Stinging cells are used to capture prey.

Crustacea
- The body is made up of two parts.
- There are 14 legs.
- Woodlice are the only crustacea that live on land.
- Crabs, lobsters and prawns are close relatives of woodlice.

Reptiles
- Skin is dry and covered with scales that restrict water loss from the body.
- Lay eggs, each protected by a hard shell.
- As a result, water is not necessary for breeding.

ANIMAL KINGDOM

Phylum Arthropoda

Class Crustacea woodlouse	Class Arachnida spider

Class Insecta fly

Phylum Cnidaria sea anemone

Phylum Chordata

Class Pisces stickleback	Class Reptilia lizard
Class Aves thrush	Class Amphibia frog

Class Mammalia human

Phylum Annelida earthworm

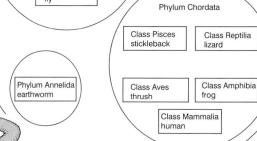

Insects
- The body is made up of three parts: head, thorax and abdomen.
- There are six legs.
- There are usually two pairs of wings, but flies have one pair.

Worms
- The body is long and thin.
- The body is made up of many segments.

Birds
- The body is covered with feathers which:
  - make flying possible
  - keep in heat
  - keep out water.
- The beak is specialised (adapted) differently in different species to deal with different foods.
- Birds lay eggs, protected by a hard shell.

Amphibians
- Live on land but breed in water.
- Young are swimming tadpoles.
- Development of young into adult is called a metamorphosis.
- Soft skin loses water easily in dry air.

Fish
- The body is covered with scales.
- Fins control the position of the body in water.
- Gills are surfaces for gaseous exchange.

Mammals
- Hair helps conserve body heat.
- Young feed on milk produced by the female's breasts (mammary glands).
- Have a small tail bone called the coccyx.

Groups within groups – the major groups of the Animal kingdom and the Plant kingdom, with an example of each. Each major group of plants is called a Division rather than a Phylum.

Mosses

- Mosses quickly lose water in dry air. As a result, mosses live in damp places.
- Roots are absent.
- As a result, water is soaked up by capillary movement over the leaves.
- Stalks grow from moss plants, each carrying a spore capsule filled with spores.
- Each spore is able to develop into a new plant.

REPRODUCE BY MEANS OF SPORES

PLANT KINGDOM

Division (= Phylum)
Mosses

Division (= Phylum)
Ferns

Division (= Phylum)
Seed plants

Class
conifers

Class
flowering plants

Ferns

- A waxy layer waterproofs the plant's surfaces, reducing water loss in a dry atmosphere.
- Roots draw water from the soil.
- Spore capsules containing spores grow in patches on the undersides of leaves.
- Each spore is able to grow into a new fern plant.

REPRODUCE BY MEANS OF SEEDS

Forget-me-not: annual – flowers and produces seed in one growing season. The plant then dies.

Oak tree: perennial – produces seeds year after year. The plant survives for many years.

Conifers

- Seeds are contained in cones.
- Covered with leaves all year round ('evergreens').
- Roots draw water from the soil.
- Waxy layer waterproofs plant surfaces.

Flowering plants

- Seeds are contained in fruits.
- Leaves of trees/shrubs fall once a year ('deciduous').
- Roots draw water from the soil.
- Waxy layer waterproofs plant surfaces.

The genus and the species identify the individual living thing, rather like your first name and surname identify you. For example, humans belong to the genus *Homo* and have the species name *sapiens*; barn owls are called *Tyto alba*.

Since the name of each living thing is in two parts, the method of naming is called the **binomial system**. Notice that the genus name begins with a capital letter, the species name begins with a small letter, and the whole name is printed in italics.

The five kingdoms

There are five kingdoms. Living things in each kingdom obtain food in different ways. Their structure and body chemistry are different. Each kingdom, therefore, represents a way of life which all its members share. Pages 12–13 show the major groups in the Animal kingdom and Plant kingdom. The other kingdoms are:

Kingdom Fungi – organisms made up of cells that form thread-like structures called **hyphae**.

Kingdom Protista – single-celled organisms.

Kingdom Bacteria – single-celled organisms. The cell body is simple in structure compared with the cell body of protists.

(not to scale)

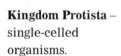

Fact file

Viruses are not cells. They do not seem to need food as a source of energy, and they cannot reproduce independently. Consisting of a strand of nucleic acid (see page 45) enclosed in a coat of protein, a virus is so small that it can only be seen using an electron microscope. Viruses infect and take over living cells to reproduce new viruses. Some types of virus cause diseases in plants and animals.

1.4 Identifying living things

preview

At the end of this section you will:
- **know that a key is a set of clues that help identify a particular organism or group of organisms**
- **understand how to use a dichotomous key**
- **know that a dichotomous key can be written in different ways.**

What is a key?

A **key** is a means of identifying an unfamiliar organism from a selection of specimens. A key consists of a set of descriptions. Each description is a clue that helps in the identification. A set of clues makes the key.

The easiest type of key to use is called a **dichotomous** key. 'Dichotomous' means branching into two. Each time the key branches, you have to choose between alternative statements. The alternative statements may be presented diagrammatically as a chart, or written in pairs or **couplets**. For example, a key to amphibians would begin:

		yes	no
1	The animal has a tail.	**newts**	go to **2**
2	The animal has no tail.	**frogs and toads**	go to **3**
	and so on …		

By comparing the pairs of statements with the organisms, you will eventually find one that fits. This identifies the organism. A key is therefore the route to a name. Different keys are used to name different living things.

When making a key, it is important to choose features that are characteristic of the type of organism rather than of the individual itself. For example, shape or proportions and patterns of colour are fairly constant in a type of organism and are therefore useful clues in a key. Size and shades of colour vary from individual to individual and are of limited use.

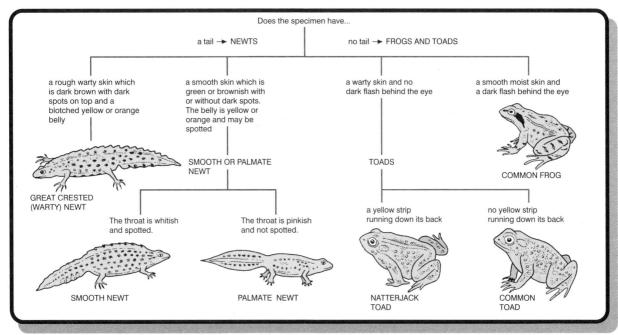

Different ways of writing a key to amphibians

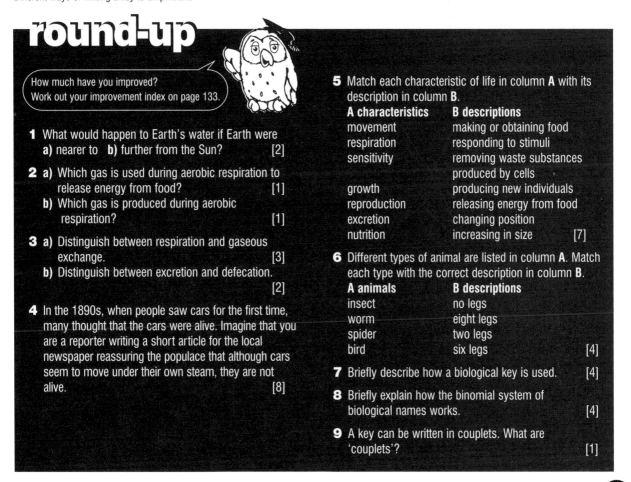

round-up

How much have you improved?
Work out your improvement index on page 133.

1 What would happen to Earth's water if Earth were
a) nearer to   b) further from the Sun?   [2]

2 a) Which gas is used during aerobic respiration to
release energy from food?   [1]
b) Which gas is produced during aerobic
respiration?   [1]

3 a) Distinguish between respiration and gaseous
exchange.   [3]
b) Distinguish between excretion and defecation.
[2]

4 In the 1890s, when people saw cars for the first time,
many thought that the cars were alive. Imagine that you
are a reporter writing a short article for the local
newspaper reassuring the populace that although cars
seem to move under their own steam, they are not
alive.   [8]

5 Match each characteristic of life in column **A** with its
description in column **B**.

A characteristics	B descriptions
movement	making or obtaining food
respiration	responding to stimuli
sensitivity	removing waste substances
	produced by cells
growth	producing new individuals
reproduction	releasing energy from food
excretion	changing position
nutrition	increasing in size [7]

6 Different types of animal are listed in column **A**. Match
each type with the correct description in column **B**.

A animals	B descriptions
insect	no legs
worm	eight legs
spider	two legs
bird	six legs [4]

7 Briefly describe how a biological key is used.   [4]

8 Briefly explain how the binomial system of
biological names works.   [4]

9 A key can be written in couplets. What are
'couplets'?   [1]

Organisms in the environment

How much do you already know?
Work out your score on pages 133–4.

Test yourself

1 Match each term in column **A** with the correct description in column **B**.

A terms	B descriptions
biosphere	the place where a group of organisms lives
community	all the ecosystems of the world
habitat	a group of individuals of the same species
population	all the organisms that live in a particular ecosystem [4]

2 a) Why is a food web a more accurate description of feeding in a community than a food chain? [2]

b) Why do food chains and food webs always begin with plants? [4]

3 a) Why is the pyramid of biomass usually a better description of a community than the pyramid of numbers? [2]

b) Why is the pyramid of energy the best description of the feeding relationships within a community? [3]

4 Give reasons for the rapid increase in the human population. [4]

5 Weigh up the benefits in food production of intensive farming against the costs to the environment. [5]

2.1 Introducing ecology

preview

At the end of this section you will understand that:

* an ecosystem is a self-contained part of the biosphere, such as a pond or an oak wood
* the community consists of the organisms that live in a particular ecosystem
* the habitat is the place where a group of organisms live
* a niche is the role each species has in its habitat
* a population is a group of organisms of the same species living in a particular place at the same time.

Some ecological terms

Ecology involves studying the relationships between organisms and between organisms and the environment.

The diagram on page 10 shows how all the places on Earth where there is life form the **biosphere**. Each organism is suited (**adapted**) to the place where it lives. This place consists of

* an **environment** of air, soil or water
* a living **community** of plants, animals, fungi and microorganisms.

Environment and community together form an **ecosystem**, which is a more or less self-contained part of the biosphere. 'Self-contained' means that each ecosystem has its own characteristic organisms not usually found in other ecosystems. These organisms are the living (**biotic**) community of the ecosystem. The physical environment is the non-living (**abiotic**) part, consisting of air, soil or water. The diagram opposite shows the different components of an oak wood ecosystem.

The flow chart below shows the hierarchy of ecological terms.

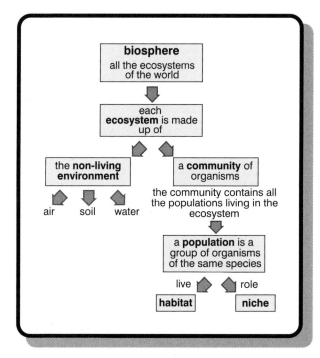

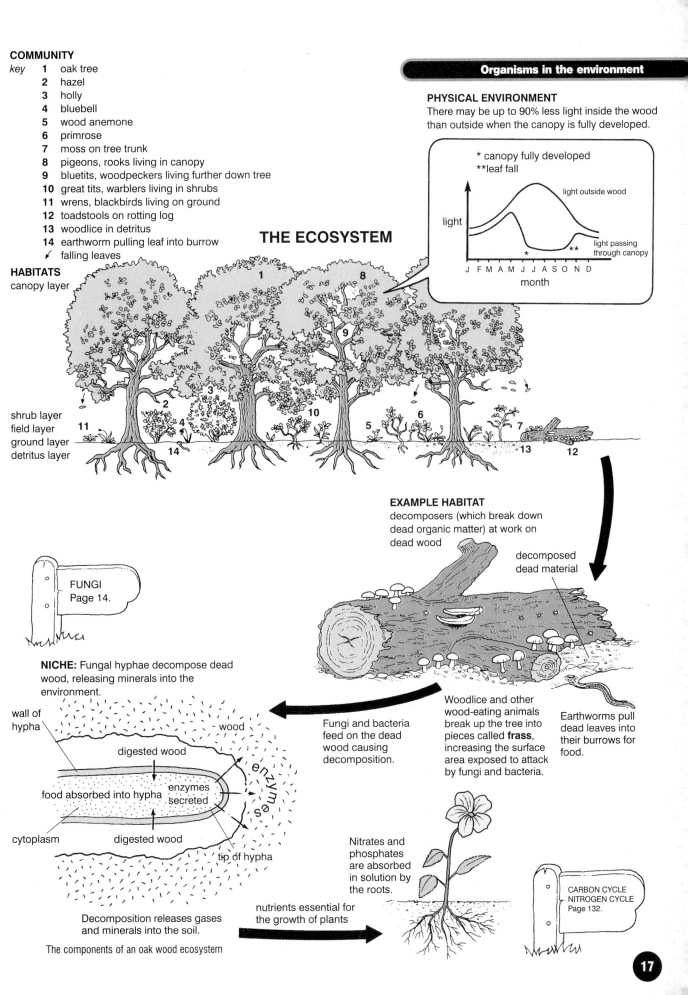

COMMUNITY

key
1 oak tree
2 hazel
3 holly
4 bluebell
5 wood anemone
6 primrose
7 moss on tree trunk
8 pigeons, rooks living in canopy
9 bluetits, woodpeckers living further down tree
10 great tits, warblers living in shrubs
11 wrens, blackbirds living on ground
12 toadstools on rotting log
13 woodlice in detritus
14 earthworm pulling leaf into burrow
↙ falling leaves

HABITATS
canopy layer

shrub layer
field layer
ground layer
detritus layer

THE ECOSYSTEM

PHYSICAL ENVIRONMENT
There may be up to 90% less light inside the wood than outside when the canopy is fully developed.

* canopy fully developed
**leaf fall

light outside wood

light

light passing through canopy

J F M A M J J A S O N D
month

EXAMPLE HABITAT
decomposers (which break down dead organic matter) at work on dead wood

decomposed dead material

FUNGI
Page 14.

NICHE: Fungal hyphae decompose dead wood, releasing minerals into the environment.

wall of hypha

wood

digested wood

food absorbed into hypha

enzymes secreted

enzymes

cytoplasm

digested wood

tip of hypha

Fungi and bacteria feed on the dead wood causing decomposition.

Woodlice and other wood-eating animals break up the tree into pieces called **frass**, increasing the surface area exposed to attack by fungi and bacteria.

Earthworms pull dead leaves into their burrows for food.

Nitrates and phosphates are absorbed in solution by the roots.

Decomposition releases gases and minerals into the soil.

nutrients essential for the growth of plants

The components of an oak wood ecosystem

CARBON CYCLE
NITROGEN CYCLE
Page 132.

2.2 Food chains and webs

preview

At the end of this section you will:

- **know the meaning of the terms producer, herbivore, carnivore and omnivore**
- **understand that energy is transferred along food chains**
- **be able to interpret diagrams of food chains and food webs.**

Who eats whom?

Finding out 'who eats whom' is one way of describing how a community works. Looking at

- animals' teeth or mouthparts
- what is in the intestine
- animals feeding
- what food an animal likes best (a **food preference test**)

helps find out what animals feed on.

The working community

Animals fall into three categories according to what they eat.

★ **Herbivores** eat plants.

★ **Carnivores** eat meat.

★ **Omnivores** eat both plants and meat. (Most human beings are omnivorous.)

Most carnivores are **predators** – they catch and eat other animals. The animals caught are called their **prey**, and are often herbivores.

Scavengers are carnivores that feed on the remains of prey left by predators, or on the bodies of animals that have died for other reasons such as disease or old age.

A **food chain** shows the links between plants, prey, predators and scavengers. Some examples of food chains are shown opposite.

Notice in each example that

- the arrows represent the transfer of food between different organisms

- the arrows point from the eaten to the eater
- the number of links in a food chain is usually four or less.

A **food web** is usually a more accurate description of feeding relationships in a community because most animals eat more than one type of plant or other animal. Some examples of food webs are shown opposite.

Notice in each example that

- several food chains link up to form a food web
- plants produce food by photosynthesis
- different types of animal eat the same type of food.

Producers

Plants, algae and some bacteria (see page 14) are called **producers** because they can use sunlight to produce food by  PHOTOSYNTHESIS Page 48.
photosynthesis. This is why food chains and food webs always begin with plants (or algae or photosynthetic bacteria). Animals use this food when they eat plants. Even when they eat other animals, predators depend on plant food indirectly since somewhere along the line the prey has been a plant eater. Because they eat food, animals are called **consumers**.

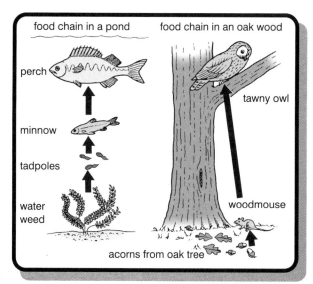

food chain in a pond • food chain in an oak wood

perch

minnow

tadpoles

water weed

tawny owl

woodmouse

acorns from oak tree

Food chains

food web in a pond

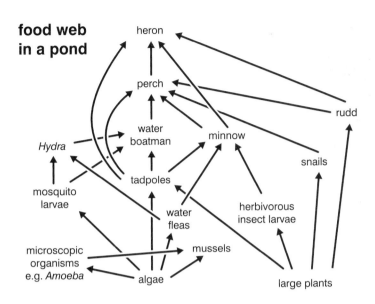

Energy flow

Sunlight underpins life on earth. Without sunlight, and the photosynthesis which depends on it, communities would cease to exist.

Through photosynthesis plants convert light energy into the chemical energy of food. A food chain represents one pathway of food energy through the community of an ecosystem. A food web represents many pathways. The diagram below shows the idea.

At each link in the food chain, energy is lost in the waste products of each living thing.

food web in an oak wood

insect-eating birds
e.g. woodpecker

fruit- and seed-
eating insects

owl   fox

woodmouse

woodlice

wood-boring
beetles

beetles

nectar-feeding
insects

fruit- and seed-
eating birds
e.g. finches

wood   bark   flowers   fruits and seeds   roots

woodland plants

Food webs

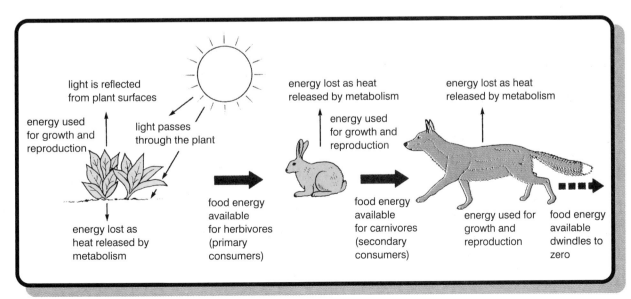

The flow of energy through a food chain

2.3 Ecological pyramids

preview

At the end of this section you will:

- understand the term trophic level
- know how to build a pyramid of numbers
- be able to interpret pyramids of numbers and pyramids of biomass
- understand that the pyramid of energy gives the best picture of the relationships between producers and consumers.

How many?

Food chains and food webs describe the feeding relationships within a community. However, they do not tell us about the numbers of individuals involved. Many plants support a limited number of herbivores which in turn support fewer carnivores.

Trophic levels

FACTS

Below is a diagram of an ecological pyramid.

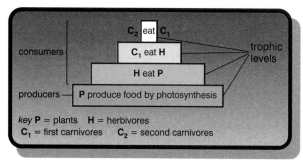

key **P** = plants   **H** = herbivores
C₁ = first carnivores   **C₂** = second carnivores

Ecological pyramid

★ The pyramid has several feeding levels called **trophic levels**.

★ Producers (plants/algae/some bacteria) occupy the base of the pyramid.

★ Other trophic levels are made up of consumers:
  - **primary** consumers are herbivores (H) that feed on plants
  - **secondary** consumers or first/primary carnivores (C_1) are carnivores that feed on herbivores
  - **tertiary** consumers or second/secondary carnivores (C_2) are carnivores which feed on first/primary carnivores.

Each trophic level groups together organisms that have similar types of food. For example, a snail and a sheep are herbivores. Both belong to the second (H) trophic level.

The group of organisms in each trophic level is smaller than the one below it. This gives the pyramid its shape.

Pyramids of numbers

Pyramids of numbers show the number of organisms in each trophic level. The table shows the numbers of insects and spiders collected from grass with a sweep net.

sample	number of insects	number of spiders
1	135	5
2	150	10
3	110	10
4	115	5
5	120	15
	630	45
	average $= \dfrac{630}{5}$ $= 126$ insects in each sample	average $= \dfrac{45}{5}$ $= 9$ spiders in each sample

Samples of insects and spiders collected with a sweep net. Each sample was collected with 10 sweeps while walking around an area of $10\,m^2$

Data like that in the table can be used to plot a pyramid of numbers, as shown below. Half the number of organisms in each trophic level is plotted on one side of the vertical line, the other half is plotted on the other side of the vertical line.

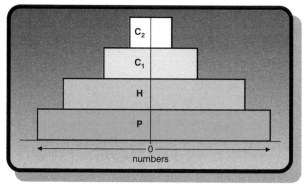

How to plot a pyramid of numbers

In grassland, the producers (grasses) and consumers (mainly insects and spiders) are small and numerous. A lot of plants support many herbivores (mostly insects) which in turn support fewer carnivores (mostly spiders). Plotting the number of organisms in each trophic level of the grassland community gives an upright pyramid that tapers to a point.

Problems with numbers ...

Example 1: the pyramid of numbers for a woodland below has a point at the bottom as well as the top. This is because relatively few producers (trees) support a large number of herbivores and carnivores. You might think that woodland consumers are in danger of starvation! However, each tree is large and can meet the food needs of many different organisms.

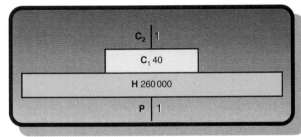

Pyramid of numbers for a woodland community

Example 2: pyramids of numbers including parasites appear top-heavy, as shown below. Many parasites feed on fewer secondary consumers.

In both these examples, number pyramids are not an accurate description of the feeding relationships in the different communities. Why? Because the pyramid of numbers does not take into account differences in size of the different producers and consumers.

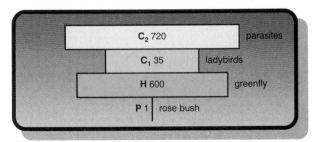

Pyramid of numbers including parasites of the secondary consumers (ladybirds)

... and the solution

A **pyramid of biomass** allows for differences in the size of organisms, because the pyramid shows the *amount of organic material* in each trophic level.

- A representative sample of the organisms at each trophic level is weighed.
- The mass is then multiplied by the estimated number of organisms in the community.

In practice, dry mass is used because fresh mass varies greatly as organisms contain different amounts of water. The sample is dried out in an oven at $110\,^{\circ}C$ until there is no further change in mass. The dry mass data is plotted as kilograms of dry mass per unit area (m^2) of the community.

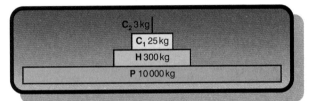

Pyramid of biomass for a woodland community

Problems with biomass ...

Example 1: the biomass of an organism can vary during the year. For example, an oak tree in full leaf during the summer will have a much greater biomass than in winter without the leaves.

Example 2: some organisms reproduce so quickly that sampling misses the rapid fluctuations in population. For example, here is an upside-down pyramid of biomass for the English Channel. Microscopic algae (producers) only live for a few days but reproduce millions of offspring very quickly. Collecting them over a short period misses this rapid turnover of living material and results in a pyramid which suggests that the biomass of herbivores (H) is greater than that of the producers (P) they feed on.

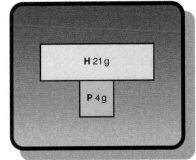

Pyramid of biomass for the English Channel, grams per unit volume (m^3) of water

... and the solution

A **pyramid of energy** gives information about the *amount of energy* at each trophic level over a certain period of time. In other words, the energy pyramid shows the amount of food being produced and consumed in a given time. Its shape therefore is not affected by differences in size, or changes in numbers of individuals.

The food energy in each trophic level is measured by incinerating samples of organisms in a **bomb calorimeter**. The heat given off is a measure of the energy value of the samples and is therefore representative of the food energy in the trophic level to which the sample of organisms belongs. The diagram below shows you the idea.

Notice that

METABOLISM
Page 11.

★ feeding transfers food energy from one trophic level to the next

★ energy is lost from each trophic level through life's activities, mostly in the form of heat released by the metabolism of cells.

As a result, the amount of food energy in a trophic level is less than the one below it.

As a result, the amount of living material (biomass) in a trophic level is less than the one below it.

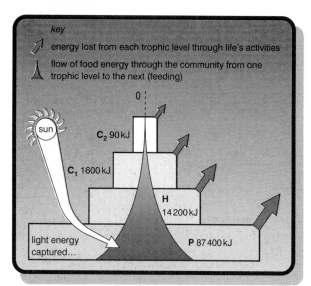

key

↗ energy lost from each trophic level through life's activities

⟍ flow of food energy through the community from one trophic level to the next (feeding)

sun

C_2 90 kJ

C_1 1600 kJ

H 14 200 kJ

light energy captured...

P 87 400 kJ

Pyramid of energy for a stream in kJ/m^2/year

2.4 Distribution of organisms

preview

At the end of this section you will:

● **understand the effect of environmental factors on the distribution of plants**

● **know that competition affects the distribution of organisms**

● **understand that different adaptations enable plants and animals to survive.**

Competition between organisms

The distribution of organisms (where living things are found in the environment) is affected by different factors.

★ Physical factors include
  • the amount of light
  • the abundance of water.

★ Biological factors include
  • **intraspecific competition** – competition between individuals of the same species
  • **interspecific competition** – competition between individuals of different species
  • **interactions** between predators and prey
  • **adaptations** of organisms for survival in different environments.

Fact file

★ **Competition:** in nature organisms that are rivals for something that is in limited supply are competitors. The 'something' is a resource like water, light, space, food or mates.

★ **Adaptation:** organisms are adapted (suited) for the environment in which they live and for their role (niche – see page 16) in that environment.

Different factors affect the distribution of organisms. Some examples follow.

Example 1: intraspecific competition for light

In a wood, the branches of full-grown trees spread in all directions. They touch the branches of neighbouring trees, forming a continuous layer. This is the **canopy** which shades out plants beneath. When a tree is blown over, light floods through the gap in the canopy, stimulating vigorous plant growth on the woodland floor. This sunlit clearing becomes an arena for intense competition between tree seedlings sprouting from thousands of seeds, and then forming saplings (young trees). Many competitors start out but there is limited space for spreading branches, which also overshadow slower-growing rivals. Many young trees perish along the way. Only the one that grows the fastest will fill the gap in the canopy, finally cutting off the sunlight that signalled the start of the race many years previously.

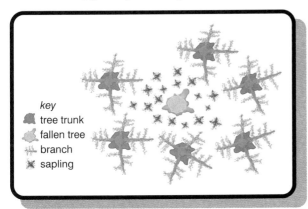

key
- tree trunk
- fallen tree
- branch
- sapling

Which sapling will survive to fill the gap? The length of the branches determines the distance between neighbouring trees, producing a continuous canopy and a regular pattern of tree trunks. The sunlit clearing caused by the fallen tree breaks the pattern and provides opportunities for new plant growth and competition between saplings to complete the canopy once more.

Example 2: intraspecific competition for water

The cacti in the photograph are widely spaced apart, and they look as if they have been planted out in a regular arrangement. The pattern appears because although many tiny cactus seedlings sprout in a particular area, there is only enough water for some of them to grow into mature plants. Growing cacti are the competitors and water is the resource in short supply.

Example 3: interspecific competition

Competition between different species is usually greatest among individuals that occupy the same trophic level. This competition for the same resource often leads to one species replacing another (called **competitive exclusion**). For example, when two species of clover (both producers) were grown separately, they grew well. However, when grown together one species eventually replaced the other. The reason was that the successful species grew slightly taller than its competitor and overshadowed it.

Example 4: predator and prey

Predators are adapted to catch prey, and prey are adapted to escape predators. The table summarises their different strategies.

predator	prey
eats a variety of prey species, reducing the risk of starvation should one prey species decline in numbers	large groups (e.g. herds of antelope, shoals of fish) distract predators from concentrating on a particular individual
catches young, old and sick prey	stings and bitter taste deter predators
catches large prey which provides more food per kill	warning coloration tells predators to avoid particular prey
moves to areas where prey is plentiful	camouflage conceals prey
	shock tactics startle predators
	prey tries to run/swim/fly faster than pursuing predator

Strategies for predator success and prey survival

Cacti in the Arizona Desert, south-western United States, where rainfall is erratic and infrequent

2.5 Population size

At the end of this section you will:
- **know how populations increase in size**
- **understand that the impact of human activity on the environment is related to population size**
- **be able to identify specific effects of human activity on the environment.**

The size of a population

★ A **population** is a group of individuals of the same species living in a particular place at the same time.

★ **Births** and **immigration** increase the size of a population.

★ **Deaths** and **emigration** decrease the size of a population.

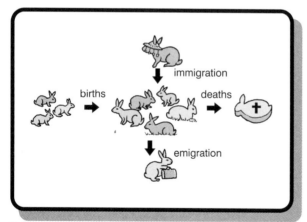

Factors affecting the size of a population

Population growth

The following graph shows that populations grow in a particular way. **Limiting factors** stop populations from growing indefinitely. They include:

shortages of
- food
- water
- oxygen
- light
- shelter

build-up of
- poisonous wastes
- predators
- disease
- social factors.

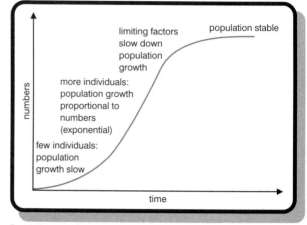

Population growth curve

Predator and prey populations

Predation affects the number of the prey population. The number of prey affects the predator population: if prey is scarce, then some of the predators will starve. The graphs below show the relationships between the numbers of predators and prey.

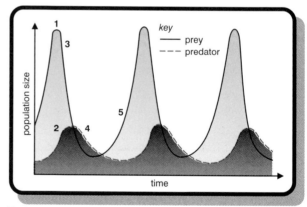

Predator–prey relationships

1 Prey breed and increase in numbers if conditions are favourable (e.g. food is abundant).

2 Predators breed and increase in numbers in response to the abundance of prey.

3 Predation pressure increases and the number of prey declines.

4 Predator numbers decline in response to the shortage of food.

5 Predation pressure decreases and so prey numbers increase ... and so on.

Notice that

- fluctuations in predator numbers are *less* than fluctuations in prey numbers
- fluctuations in predator numbers *lag* behind fluctuations in prey numbers.

Why is this? There are fewer predators than prey, and predators tend to reproduce more slowly than prey.

The human population

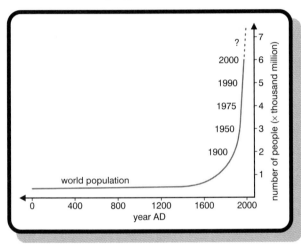

World population growth over the past 2000 years showing predicted future increase based on present trends

This graph shows that the human population has grown dramatically since the beginning of the nineteenth century. Although the populations of Europe, North America and Japan (developed countries) are levelling off, the populations of Latin America, Asia and Africa (developing countries) are still growing rapidly as a result of

- improvements in food production
- more drugs for the treatment of disease
- improved medical care
- improved public health.

The rate of population growth is affected by the number of young people in the population, particularly women of child-bearing age. The table summarises the problem.

A large proportion of the world's population is young so the problems listed in the table are global. The problems are particularly acute in developing countries.

problem	result
present birth rate high	adding to the rate of population increase
future birth rate high	as children in the population 'bulge' grow older and have their own children, adding further to the rate of population increase
social services inadequate	large numbers of children put strain on the educational system, medical services and housing

Problems of a young population

In Britain (and other developed countries) the problems are more to do with a population that has an increasing proportion of old people. The diseases of old age (cancer, arthritis, dementia) take up an increasing proportion of the resources available for medical care.

Human impact on the environment

1.5 million years ago: early humans probably moved from place to place in search of food. They hunted animals and gathered plants. Their impact on the environment was no more than that of other medium-sized animals.

10 000 years ago: about 12 million people lived in the world. In the Middle East they harvested wild wheat and other grains. When the grain was ripe, a family could probably gather over a year's supply in just a few weeks. People had little impact on the environment beyond their village.

2000 years ago: people had started to farm. Skills in crafts and tool-making developed. Villages became larger and some grew into towns. People had a much greater impact on the environment – farming the land, using raw materials.

Today: about 6 billion (thousand million) people live in the world. In developed countries, food is produced by relatively few people. Industry and technology use raw materials, often obtained from developing countries where environments may be stripped of resources. Pages 26–7 show the impact of human activities on today's environment.

2

Resources are the raw materials needed to satisfy human demands for food, homes, hospitals, schools and manufactured goods.

RESOURCES

• **Renewable resources** are replaced as fast as plants and animals can reproduce and grow. If a resource is over-used it will decline. Damage to the environment also limits the production of renewable resources.

CASE STUDY: Fishing in the North Sea

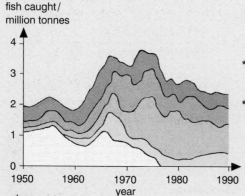

fish caught/ million tonnes

year

key

other species e.g. plaice

cod and haddock

small species used commercially

mackerel

herring

Catches of fish are reduced because of:
* **overfishing:** increased efficiency of fishing methods catches more fish than are replaced by reproduction
* **pollution:**
  • nutrients (e.g. nitrogen and phosphorus) from sewage works and surplus artificial fertilisers enter rivers which discharge into the North Sea
  • pesticides used to protect crops enter rivers which discharge into the North Sea
  • metals (e.g. mercury, cadmium, copper) from different industrial processes

---

• **Non-renewable resources** cannot be replaced when used up. For example, there are only limited amounts of fossil fuels (coal, oil, natural gas) and metals.

CASE STUDY: World reserves of metals
The table shows estimated world reserves of some metals vital for the manufacture of goods and technological development. Work out how long reserves of each metal will last at present rates of use.

iron ore	annual use	1.6 billion tonnes
	reserves	216.4 billion tonnes
copper	annual use	10 million tonnes
	reserves	570 million tonnes
tin	annual use	226 thousand tonnes
	reserves	4.2 million tonnes

Tin: 19 years
Copper: 57 years
Iron ore: 135 years
Answers (to the nearest whole number)

FARMING
Page 28.

How human activities exploit resources and land and produce pollution

Land use destroys habitats, driving thousands of species of
plants and animals to the verge of extinction. The pressures are
- economic development
- growing human populations } increase the use of land
- the increasing need for food to feed people.

CASE STUDY 1: Land use in the United Kingdom
Out of 24 million hectares of land in the UK:
- 19 million hectares are used for agriculture
- 1.7 million hectares are used for housing.
Quarrying (gravel, limestone, sand and sandstone) for building materials
and the disposal of household waste account for some of the rest.

CASE STUDY 2: Exploiting tropical rainforest
Rainforests girdle the equator covering 14.5 million km^2 of land.
The vegetation recycles carbon dioxide and oxygen through
photosynthesis.
Moisture absorbed by the forest evaporates back into the
atmosphere, to fall as rain thousands of miles away. Rainforest
is being cleared at a rate of 100 000 km^2 each year for:

cheap beef is exported to
be made into hamburgers

Beef: about 20 000 km^2
of Brazilian forest are
cleared each year
for cattle ranches.

POLLUTION

Opencast mining for
metals causes much
damage to rainforest.

After clearing, nutrients
disappear and soil is
soon exhausted.
Semi-desert develops:
the ranchers move on to
clear a new area.

Logging: only 4% of trees
are felled for timber, but
another 40% are damaged
or destroyed in the process.

Pollution is the result of industry making goods that maintain our standard of living.
- **Air** is polluted by gases, dust and smoke from vehicles and industry.
- **Water** is polluted by wastes from factories and runoff of agrochemicals.
- **Land** is polluted by agrochemicals and the dumping of rubbish and waste.

CASE STUDY: Environmental
problems caused by pollution

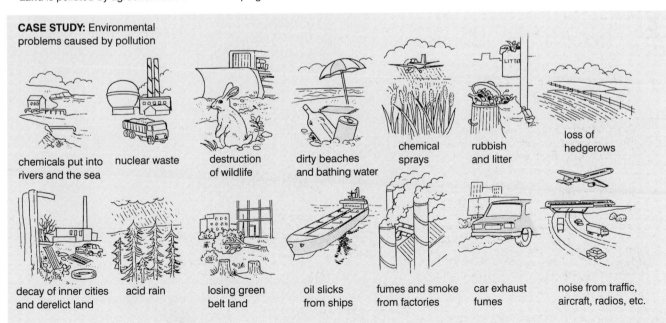

chemicals put into
rivers and the sea

nuclear waste

destruction
of wildlife

dirty beaches
and bathing water

chemical
sprays

rubbish
and litter

loss of
hedgerows

decay of inner cities
and derelict land

acid rain

losing green
belt land

oil slicks
from ships

fumes and smoke
from factories

car exhaust
fumes

noise from traffic,
aircraft, radios, etc.

2.6 Food production

At the end of this section you will:

- **understand why a short food chain makes more food energy available to the consumer than a long food chain**
- **know that intensive farming produces food in great quantities.**

Fact file

★ **Intensive farming** means that farmers use different methods to produce as much food as possible from the land available for raising crops (**arable** farming) and the land available for raising animals (**livestock** farming).

★ **Productivity** means the amount of food produced (crops or livestock) per unit area of land (e.g. per hectare (ha)).

Energy and farming

Farms are ecosystems with people as consumers in a food chain of crops and livestock. The amount of food a farm produces depends on

- the amount of energy entering the farm ecosystem
- the efficiency with which energy is converted into plant and animal tissue.

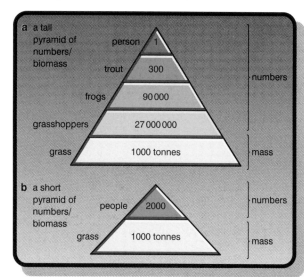

Eating trout and eating vegetables

Do you like trout? The pyramid that supports one person's appetite for trout is shown, along with another pyramid showing the number of people supported who are vegetarian. (Remember that cereals are varieties of cultivated grass.)

Shortening the food chain

The inefficiency of energy transfer between trophic levels accounts for the difference between pyramids **a** and **b**. The *fewer* the trophic levels (links in a food chain), the *less* food energy is lost and so the *more* food is available to consumers.

Energy transfer between producers and consumers is inefficient because

- some of the plant material is not digested and passes out of the herbivore body as faeces
- the herbivore uses energy to stay alive
- when the herbivore dies, its body represents 'locked up' energy, some of which transfers to decomposers.

Eating meat is therefore wasteful in terms of food energy.

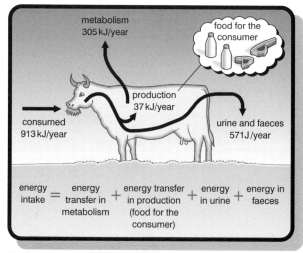

Wasting energy

Farming

The concept map for **food production** on page 30 shows different technologies at work on the modern intensive farm. The checklist points opposite summarise the benefits for food production but also highlight the impact on the environment and the possible risks to public health.

Checklist for intensive farming

checklist	benefits	impact
1 pesticides	kill pests which damage crops	spray is carried in the wind (drift) which can harm wildlife
	food production increases	pesticide runoff seeps into groundwater, eventually draining into ponds and river systems, possibly contaminating drinking water and harming wildlife
2 irrigation	brings water to land	salination: the Sun's heat evaporates water, increasing the concentration of mineral salts in soil. Eventually land is too 'salty' for crops to grow, reducing crop yields
	food production increases	overwatering: land becomes waterlogged, reducing crop yields. In warm countries the threat to public health increases because habitats are created for the spread of water-borne diseases such as malaria and schistosomiasis
3 mechanisation	powerful machinery needs few people to work it, cutting wage costs	land is cleared of woods and hedges to make fields larger – large machinery is most efficient in big fields
	more land can be used for farming	habitats are destroyed with loss of wildlife
	harvests crop more quickly	soil is packed, causing waterlogging
4 manure	spreading manure on land adds humus which improves soil structure	water is needed to wash manure into lagoon
		slurry leaks from lagoon, seeping into streams and rivers, kill fish and other wildlife
5 monoculture	efficient use of expensive machinery	crop provides unlimited food for consumer populations, which increase to pest proportions
	reduces labour costs	costs are high because crops must be sprayed with pesticides
	high yields mean farmer can take advantage of selling in bulk to obtain best prices for produce	soil loses its nutrients which are replaced with expensive artificial fertilisers
		soil is left bare between crops, risking erosion
6 artificial fertilisers	land can be used continuously for growing crops	manufacture of fertilisers uses a lot of fuel
	farmers do not need to keep animals for manure	soil structure deteriorates and soil erosion increases
	efficiency is increased by specialising in growing one or two crops each year	surplus fertiliser runs off into streams and rivers: this encourages population explosion of algae (called blooms) which use up oxygen in the water, killing wildlife. Surplus fertiliser may also put excess nitrates, a health hazard, into drinking water
	food production is increased, helping feed the world's growing population	

Biology Revision Guide

Pests are plants and animals that destroy crops and livestock or prevent land from being used for farming.

Pesticides are chemicals that kill pests. Pesticides are very poisonous if accidentally swallowed. Some can cause illnesses when eaten in food. There are three types of pesticide:

- **insecticides** kill insects
- **herbicides** kill weeds (plants that compete with crops for space, light and nutrients)
- **fungicides** kill fungi.

Farmers apply pesticides as sprays, dusts, dips, fogs or granules.

Irrigation brings water to land that would otherwise be too dry to grow crops. It also improves yields where rainfall is low. Today, over 2 million km^2 of irrigated land produce about 30% of the world's food. Estimates predict that more than 3 million km^2 of land will be irrigated by the end of the twentieth century.

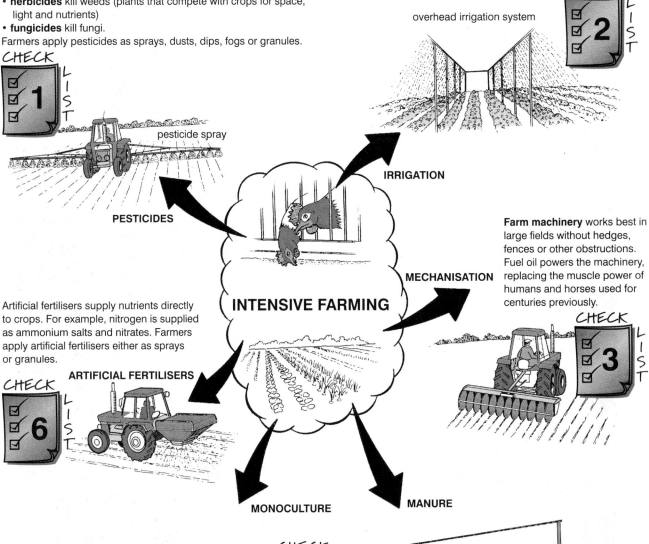

overhead irrigation system

IRRIGATION

pesticide spray

PESTICIDES

INTENSIVE FARMING

MECHANISATION

Farm machinery works best in large fields without hedges, fences or other obstructions. Fuel oil powers the machinery, replacing the muscle power of humans and horses used for centuries previously.

Artificial fertilisers supply nutrients directly to crops. For example, nitrogen is supplied as ammonium salts and nitrates. Farmers apply artificial fertilisers either as sprays or granules.

ARTIFICIAL FERTILISERS

MONOCULTURE

MANURE

Growing a large area of a single crop is called **monoculture**. The same crop is often grown year after year. Intensive arable farms specialise in monocultures of a limited number of crops.

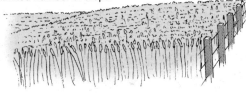

The intensive farm at work

dung drops through slats in floor

manure

washed to lagoon

Large numbers of animals reared intensively indoors produce large amounts of **manure**. Washed into pits called lagoons, the manure forms a liquid slurry.

round-up

How much have you improved?
Work out your improvement index on page 134.

1 Look at pages 16–17. List the different components of an ecosystem. [6]

2 a) Explain the meaning of the word 'abiotic'. [1]
 b) Why is the amount of light an important abiotic influence on life inside a wood? [4]

3 Look at the pond food chain on page 18.
 a) How many links are there in the food chain? [1]
 b) Name the producers. [1]
 c) Briefly explain why they are called producers. [1]
 d) Name the herbivores. [1]
 e) Briefly explain why they are called herbivores. [1]
 f) Name the carnivores. [2]
 g) Briefly explain why they are called carnivores. [1]

4 Why is the efficiency of energy conversion in photosynthesis less than 8%? [3]

5 In what circumstances is the pyramid of numbers an accurate description of the feeding relationships in a community? [1]

6 The diagram shows a pyramid of biomass for a rocky seashore.
 a) Name the producers. [1]
 b) Name the secondary consumers. [1]
 c) Severe weather conditions virtually wipe out the periwinkles. What will be the effect on the biomass of dog whelks and saw wrack? [2]

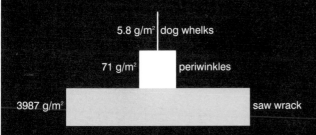

5.8 g/m² dog whelks

71 g/m² periwinkles

3987 g/m² saw wrack

7 Explain the differences between
 a) intraspecific competition and interspecific competition
 b) adaptation and survival
 c) camouflage and warning coloration. [6]

8 The graph shows long-term changes in the numbers of snowshoe hare and its predator the Canadian lynx.

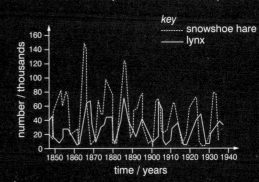

key
------- snowshoe hare
——— lynx

number / thousands

time / years

 a) Why do the highs and lows in the numbers of lynx lag behind the highs and lows in the numbers of snowshoe hare? [3]
 b) Although the numbers of snowshoe hare and lynx fluctuated between 1850 and 1940, what do you think is the *overall* trend in the population growth of each species between these years? [1]
 c) In 1890, if disease had virtually wiped out the lynx population, what do you think would have happened to the numbers of snowshoe hare? [1]
 d) If the lynx population had recovered from the effects of disease by 1910, what then do you think would have happened to the numbers of snowshoe hare? [2]
 e) If the lynx population had never recovered from the effects of disease, what then do you think would have happened to the numbers of snowshoe hare? Briefly explain your answer. [2]

9 The terms in column **A** refer to different aspects of intensive farming. Match each term with its correct description in column **B**.

A terms	B descriptions
fertiliser	kills plants
herbicide	an unwanted plant
irrigation	supplies plants with nutrients
monoculture	supplies plants with water
weed	a crop plant grown over a large area [5]

Well done if you've improved. Don't worry if you haven't. Take a break and try again.

Cell activity

3

Work out your score on pages 134–5.

Test yourself

1 Match each of the structures in column **A** with its function in column **B**.

A structures   **B functions**

mitochondrion   partially permeable to substances in solution

cell membrane   where energy is released from the oxidation of glucose

chloroplast   fully permeable to substances in solution

cell wall   contains the chromosomes

nucleus   where light energy is captured

[5]

2 Why do you think the process of active transport requires more energy than diffusion? [1]

3 Explain the difference between
  a) a plasmolysed cell and a turgid cell [4]
  b) a fully permeable membrane and a partially permeable membrane. [3]

4 What is a clone? [1]

5 What is formed by the replication of DNA? [2]

6 a) Why do the cells of a tissue undergo mitosis?
  b) In mitosis, what is the relationship between the number and type of chromosomes in the parent cell and in the daughter cells? [5]

7 Briefly explain the meaning of 'haploid' and 'diploid'. [4]

8 Complete the following paragraph using the words below. Each word may be used once, more than once or not at all.

types organism tissues organs cells an organ

Living things are made of _____ . Groups of similar _____ with similar functions form _____ that can work together as _____ . A group of _____ working together form _____ system. [6]

9 Cellulose and chitin are important building materials in living things. Give an example of the use of each. [2]

10 Briefly explain the difference between saturated and unsaturated fats. [2]

11 What is a nucleotide? [4]

3.1 Cells at work

preview

At the end of this section you will know that:

● **all living things are made of cells**

● **plant cells and animal cells have structures in common but are also different from one another**

● **mitochondria and chloroplasts are structures in cells which convert energy from one form to another**

● **different types of cells are each specialised to perform a particular biological task.**

Cell functions

The structures that make up a cell are organised in a way that depends on the **functions** of the cell (the way it works).

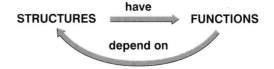

Fact file

★ Most cells are too small to be seen with the naked eye.

★ The light microscope helps us see the structure of cells.

★ The transmission electron microscope reveals cell structures too small to be seen under the light microscope. It enables us to see the fine structure of cells in great detail.

★ The human body is constructed from more than 200 different types of cell.

How cells work

The diagram on pages 34–5 is the concept map for **cells at work**. The numbers on the diagram refer to the checklist of points.

3.2 Into and out of cells

At the end of this section you will:
- **understand that there is constant movement of solutions inside and into and out of cells**
- **know about diffusion, osmosis and active transport**
- **know that solutions move along a concentration gradient.**

Moving molecules

Cells need a non-stop supply of water and the substances dissolved in it to stay alive. Substances therefore move inside and into and out of cells. They move in one of three ways.

★ **diffusion** – the movement of a substance through a solution or gas *down* a concentration gradient (that is, from a region of high concentration to a region of low concentration)

★ **osmosis** – the movement of **water** *down* a concentration gradient through a **partially permeable** membrane

★ **active transport** – the movement of a substance through a solution *up* (against) a concentration gradient (that is, from a region of low concentration to a region of high concentration).

Fact file

★ Why does sugar sprinkled onto strawberries turn pink? Because it makes the juice come out of the strawberries.

In and out of cells

On page 36 is the concept map for **Movement into and out of cells**. The numbers on the concept map refer to the checklist of points below.

Checklist for movement in and out of cells

1 ★ The molecules of a substance move at random, but there is a better than even chance that some molecules will spread from where they are highly concentrated to where they are fewer in number.

As a result, there is a net movement of molecules from where the substance is in high concentration to where it is in low concentration.

★ Diffusion continues until the concentration of the substance is the same throughout the gas or solution.

★ The greater the difference in concentration between the regions, the steeper the concentration gradient and the faster the substance diffuses.

2 ★ In active transport, the molecules of a substance move in the reverse direction to normal diffusion.

As a result, cells may build up stores of a substance which would otherwise be spread out by diffusion.

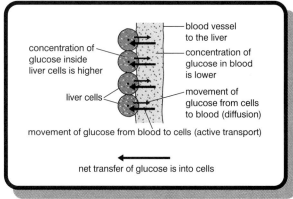

Glucose is stored in the liver by active transport

★ Active transport requires more energy than normal diffusion.

3 ★ The flow of water from a more dilute solution to a more concentrated solution is called osmosis.

★ A partially permeable membrane allows some substances to pass through but stops others. The passage of substances across such a membrane depends on the
- size of the molecules
- size of the membrane pores
- surface area of the cell membrane
- rate of diffusion.

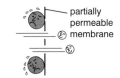

★ The changes happening inside plant cells due to osmosis bring about visible changes in the plant.
- Plasmolysis causes a plant to **wilt** through lack of water.
- The plant recovers following watering, which restores turgor to its cells.

★ Osmosis through a partially permeable membrane continues until the concentrations of water on either side of the membrane are equal.

Checklist for cells at work

1 ★ During photosynthesis, oxygen is released into the environment.

★ During aerobic respiration, oxygen is used to release energy from food.

As a result, photosynthesis and aerobic respiration are stages in a cycle, the by-products of one forming the starting point of the other.

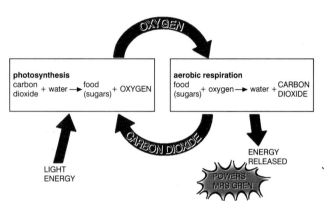

The oxygen–carbon dioxide cycle

2 ★ There are different types of cell for different functions.

★ Each type of cell is suited (**adapted**) for its function in the animal body or plant body.

★ A sheet of cells which covers a body surface is called an **epithelium**.

★ Red blood cells do not have nuclei.

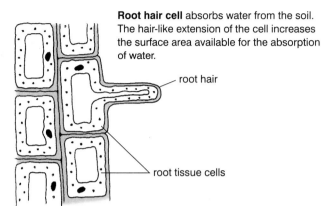

Root hair cell absorbs water from the soil. The hair-like extension of the cell increases the surface area available for the absorption of water.

root hair

root tissue cells

Red blood cells transport oxygen around the body. They contain haemoglobin which combines with oxygen.

flattened disc shape increases surface area for the absorption of oxygen

VARIETY OF CELLS

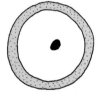

sperm – the male sex cell which swims to the egg

tail-like flagellum lashes from side to side

ovum (egg) – the female sex cell which is fertilised when a sperm fuses with it

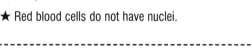

Ciliated cells – cilia are rows of fine hairs which sway to and fro. Ciliated cells line the windpipe. They sweep a covering layer of mucus, which traps bacteria, viruses and other particles, into the pharynx. The mucus is either swallowed, sneezed out or coughed up.

cilia

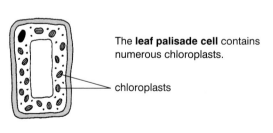

The **leaf palisade cell** contains numerous chloroplasts.

chloroplasts

Xylem cells form tubes in the stem, roots and leaves, transporting water to all parts of the plant.

Cells at work

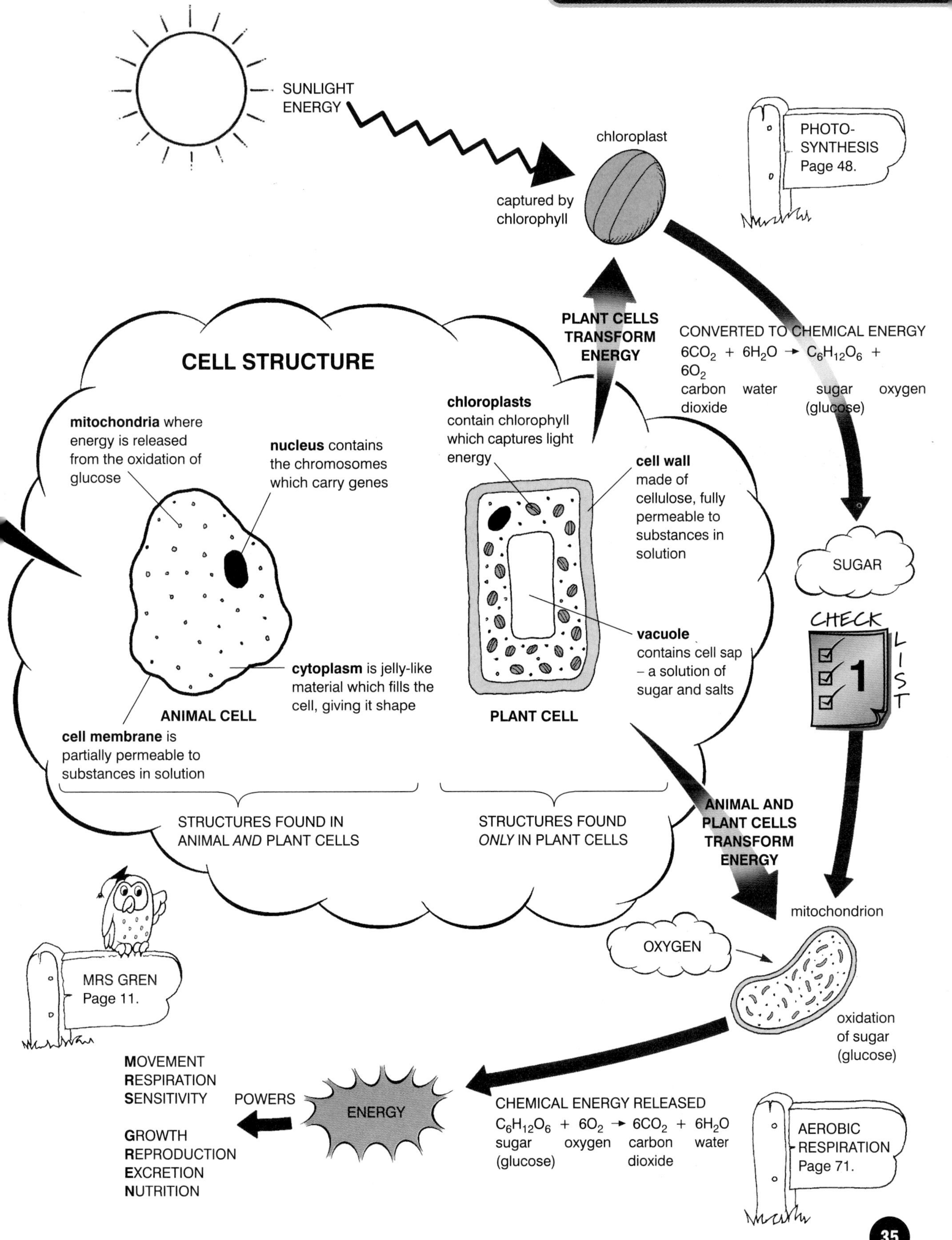

SUNLIGHT
ENERGY

chloroplast

captured by
chlorophyll

PHOTO-
SYNTHESIS
Page 48.

**PLANT CELLS
TRANSFORM
ENERGY**

CONVERTED TO CHEMICAL ENERGY
$6CO_2 + 6H_2O \rightarrow C_6H_{12}O_6 + 6O_2$
carbon   water   sugar   oxygen
dioxide   (glucose)

CELL STRUCTURE

mitochondria where
energy is released
from the oxidation of
glucose

nucleus contains
the chromosomes
which carry genes

chloroplasts
contain chlorophyll
which captures light
energy

cell wall
made of
cellulose, fully
permeable to
substances in
solution

SUGAR

CHECK
LIST
☑
☑ **1**
☑

cytoplasm is jelly-like
material which fills the
cell, giving it shape

vacuole
contains cell sap
– a solution of
sugar and salts

ANIMAL CELL

PLANT CELL

cell membrane is
partially permeable to
substances in solution

STRUCTURES FOUND IN
ANIMAL *AND* PLANT CELLS

STRUCTURES FOUND
ONLY IN PLANT CELLS

**ANIMAL AND
PLANT CELLS
TRANSFORM
ENERGY**

MRS GREN
Page 11.

mitochondrion

OXYGEN

oxidation
of sugar
(glucose)

MOVEMENT
RESPIRATION
SENSITIVITY

POWERS

ENERGY

GROWTH
REPRODUCTION
EXCRETION
NUTRITION

CHEMICAL ENERGY RELEASED
$C_6H_{12}O_6 + 6O_2 \rightarrow 6CO_2 + 6H_2O$
sugar   oxygen   carbon   water
(glucose)   dioxide

AEROBIC
RESPIRATION
Page 71.

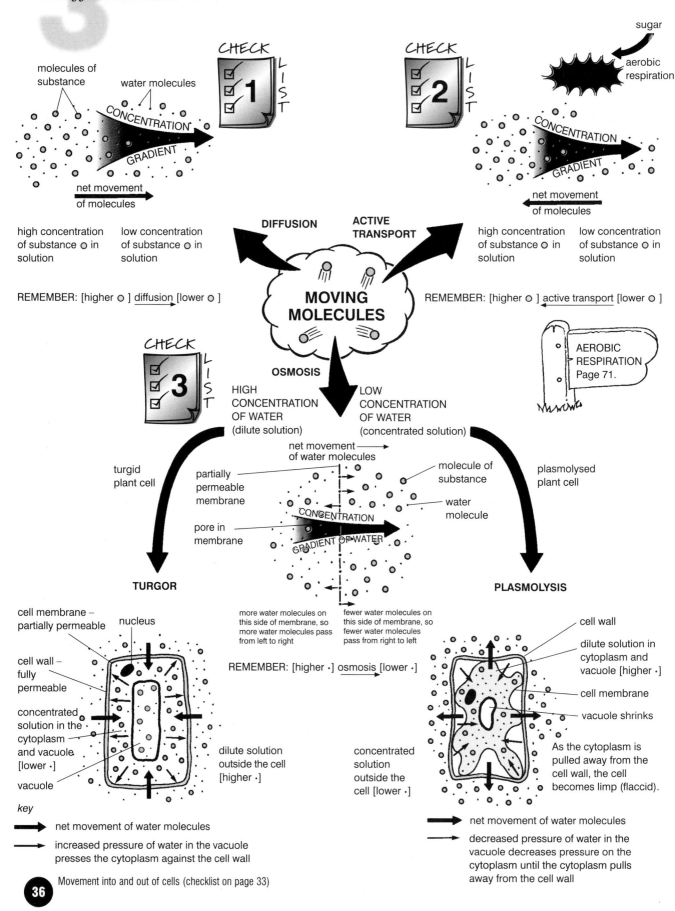

DIFFUSION

ACTIVE TRANSPORT

CHECK LIST **1**

molecules of substance

water molecules

CONCENTRATION GRADIENT

net movement of molecules

high concentration of substance ⊙ in solution

low concentration of substance ⊙ in solution

REMEMBER: [higher ⊙] diffusion [lower ⊙]

CHECK LIST **2**

sugar

aerobic respiration

CONCENTRATION GRADIENT

net movement of molecules

high concentration of substance ⊙ in solution

low concentration of substance ⊙ in solution

REMEMBER: [higher ⊙] active transport [lower ⊙]

MOVING MOLECULES

AEROBIC RESPIRATION Page 71.

OSMOSIS

CHECK LIST **3**

HIGH CONCENTRATION OF WATER (dilute solution)

LOW CONCENTRATION OF WATER (concentrated solution)

net movement of water molecules

turgid plant cell

partially permeable membrane

molecule of substance

water molecule

pore in membrane

CONCENTRATION GRADIENT OF WATER

plasmolysed plant cell

TURGOR

PLASMOLYSIS

more water molecules on this side of membrane, so more water molecules pass from left to right

fewer water molecules on this side of membrane, so fewer water molecules pass from right to left

REMEMBER: [higher ·] osmosis [lower ·]

cell membrane – partially permeable

nucleus

cell wall – fully permeable

concentrated solution in the cytoplasm and vacuole [lower ·]

vacuole

dilute solution outside the cell [higher ·]

cell wall

dilute solution in cytoplasm and vacuole [higher ·]

cell membrane

vacuole shrinks

concentrated solution outside the cell [lower ·]

As the cytoplasm is pulled away from the cell wall, the cell becomes limp (flaccid).

key

net movement of water molecules

increased pressure of water in the vacuole presses the cytoplasm against the cell wall

net movement of water molecules

decreased pressure of water in the vacuole decreases pressure on the cytoplasm until the cytoplasm pulls away from the cell wall

3.3 Cell division

preview

How cells divide

On pages 38–9 is the concept map for **cell division**. Study it carefully.

Remember

★ The **cells of the body** divide by **mitosis**.

★ The **cells of the sex organs** that give rise to the sex cells (**gametes**) divide by **meiosis**. Sex cells are produced in the sex organs:
- the testes of the male and the ovaries of the female in mammals
- the anthers (male) and the carpels (female) in flowering plants.

Mitosis and meiosis

The nucleus contains **chromosomes**, each consisting of **deoxyribonucleic acid** (**DNA**) wound round a core of protein. In cell division, the chromosomes are passed from the **parent** cell to the new **daughter** cells. 'Daughter' does not mean that the cells are female. It means that they are the new cells formed as a result of cell division.

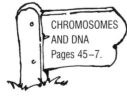

Mitosis produces daughter cells with the same number of chromosomes as the parent cell. The daughter cells are described as **diploid** (or **2n**).

Meiosis produces daughter cells with only half the number of chromosomes in the parent cell. The daughter cells are described as **haploid** (or **n**).

The importance of mitosis

The daughter cells each receive an identical full (diploid) set of chromosomes from the parent cell.

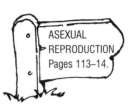

 As a result, the parent cell and its daughter cells are genetically identical. They form a **clone**.

 As a result, mitosis is the way in which living things

- **repair damage:** for example, mitosis replaces damaged skin cells with identical new skin cells
- **grow:** for example, the root of a plant grows because root tip cells divide by mitosis to form new root tissue

- **reproduce asexually:** for example, parts of stems can sprout roots and grow into new plants. The new individuals are genetically identical to the parents and are therefore clones.

The importance of meiosis

The daughter cells each receive a half (haploid) set of chromosomes from the parent cell.

 As a result, during fertilisation (when sperm and egg join together), the chromosomes from each cell combine.

 As a result, the fertilised egg (**zygote**) is diploid but inherits a new combination of genes contributed (50:50) from the parents.

As a result, the new individual inherits characteristics from both parents, not just from one parent as in asexual reproduction.

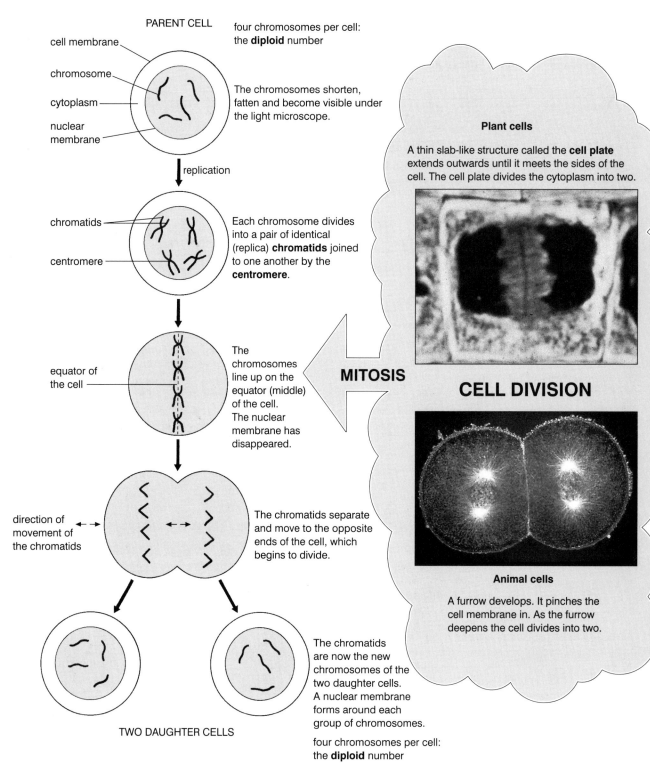

PARENT CELL

four chromosomes per cell: the **diploid** number

cell membrane
chromosome
cytoplasm
nuclear membrane

The chromosomes shorten, fatten and become visible under the light microscope.

replication

chromatids
centromere

Each chromosome divides into a pair of identical (replica) **chromatids** joined to one another by the **centromere**.

equator of the cell

The chromosomes line up on the equator (middle) of the cell. The nuclear membrane has disappeared.

direction of movement of the chromatids

The chromatids separate and move to the opposite ends of the cell, which begins to divide.

TWO DAUGHTER CELLS

The chromatids are now the new chromosomes of the two daughter cells. A nuclear membrane forms around each group of chromosomes.

four chromosomes per cell: the **diploid** number

MITOSIS

CELL DIVISION

Plant cells

A thin slab-like structure called the **cell plate** extends outwards until it meets the sides of the cell. The cell plate divides the cytoplasm into two.

Animal cells

A furrow develops. It pinches the cell membrane in. As the furrow deepens the cell divides into two.

Cell division

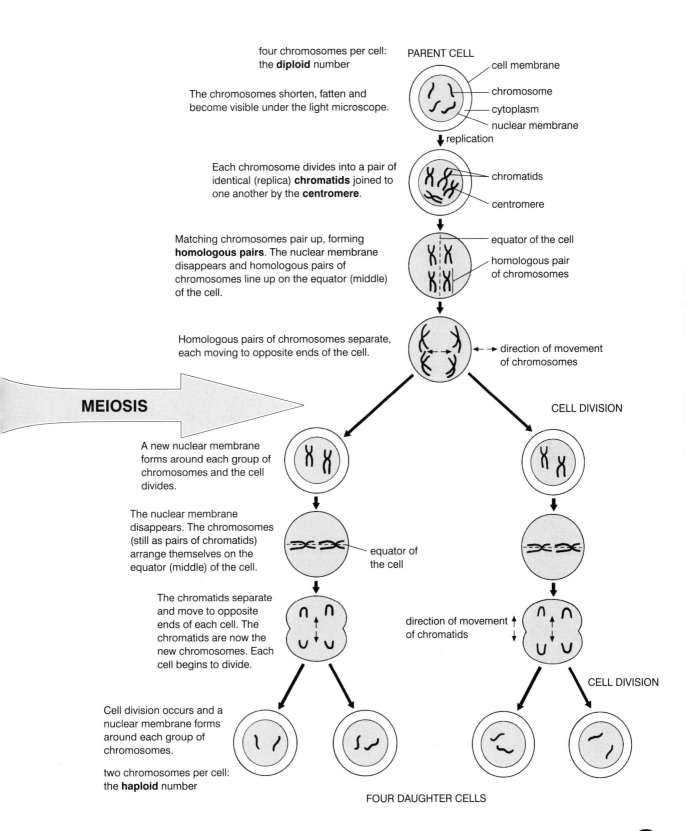

four chromosomes per cell:
the **diploid** number

PARENT CELL

cell membrane

chromosome

cytoplasm

nuclear membrane

The chromosomes shorten, fatten and
become visible under the light microscope.

replication

Each chromosome divides into a pair of
identical (replica) **chromatids** joined to
one another by the **centromere**.

chromatids

centromere

Matching chromosomes pair up, forming
homologous pairs. The nuclear membrane
disappears and homologous pairs of
chromosomes line up on the equator (middle)
of the cell.

equator of the cell

homologous pair
of chromosomes

Homologous pairs of chromosomes separate,
each moving to opposite ends of the cell.

direction of movement
of chromosomes

MEIOSIS

CELL DIVISION

A new nuclear membrane
forms around each group of
chromosomes and the cell
divides.

The nuclear membrane
disappears. The chromosomes
(still as pairs of chromatids)
arrange themselves on the
equator (middle) of the cell.

equator of
the cell

The chromatids separate
and move to opposite
ends of each cell. The
chromatids are now the
new chromosomes. Each
cell begins to divide.

direction of movement
of chromatids

CELL DIVISION

Cell division occurs and a
nuclear membrane forms
around each group of
chromosomes.

two chromosomes per cell:
the **haploid** number

FOUR DAUGHTER CELLS

3.4 Cells, tissues and organs

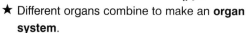

preview

At the end of this section you will:

● **understand that cells are organised into tissues, tissues into organs, and organs into organ systems**

● **know about the importance of the surface area to volume ratio for living processes**

● **understand that organ systems are specialised for exchanging materials.**

Building an organ system

Here is the concept map which revises **cells**, **tissues** and **organs**.

Plants and animals are **multicellular**: they are made of many types of cells. Each type of cell is specialised to perform a particular biological task.

★ A group of similar cells makes a **tissue**.

VARIETY OF CELLS Page 34.

★ Different tissues together make up an **organ**.

★ Different organs combine to make an **organ system**.

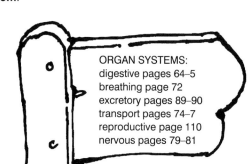

ORGAN SYSTEMS:
digestive pages 64–5
breathing page 72
excretory pages 89–90
transport pages 74–7
reproductive page 110
nervous pages 79–81

The heart and blood vessels transport blood to all parts of the body.

ANIMAL (human)

function

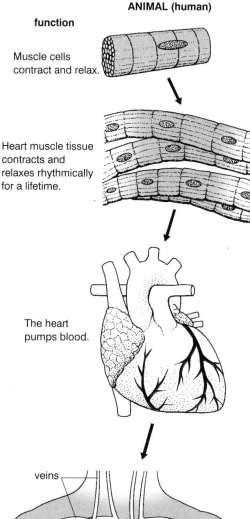

Muscle cells contract and relax.

Heart muscle tissue contracts and relaxes rhythmically for a lifetime.

The heart pumps blood.

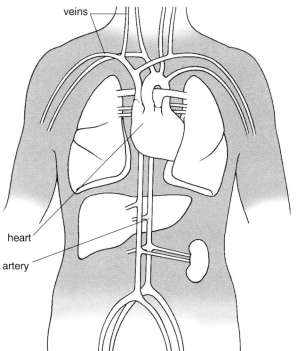

veins

heart

artery

Cells to organ systems

BUILDING AN ORGAN SYSTEM

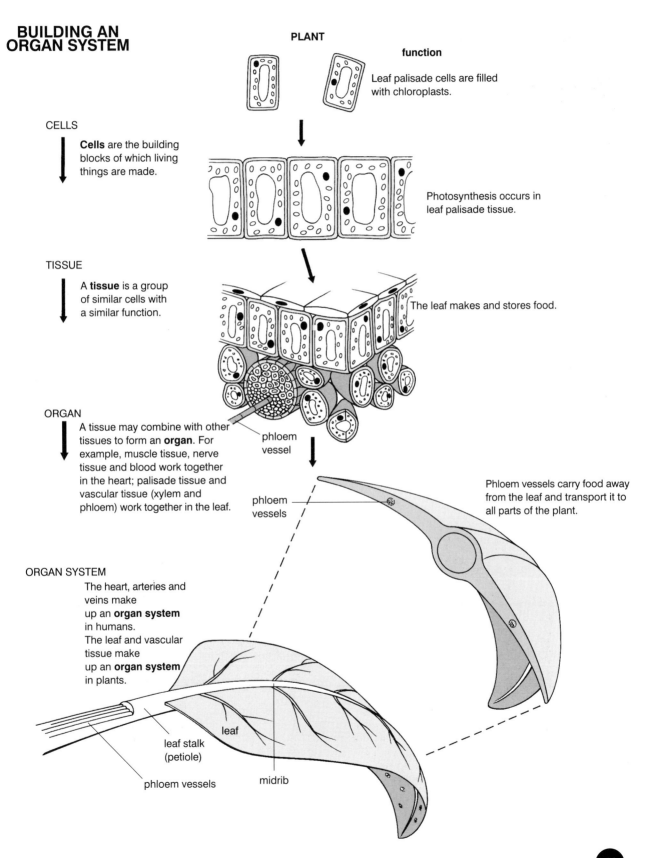

PLANT

function

Leaf palisade cells are filled with chloroplasts.

CELLS

Cells are the building blocks of which living things are made.

Photosynthesis occurs in leaf palisade tissue.

TISSUE

A **tissue** is a group of similar cells with a similar function.

The leaf makes and stores food.

ORGAN

A tissue may combine with other tissues to form an **organ**. For example, muscle tissue, nerve tissue and blood work together in the heart; palisade tissue and vascular tissue (xylem and phloem) work together in the leaf.

phloem vessel

phloem vessels

Phloem vessels carry food away from the leaf and transport it to all parts of the plant.

ORGAN SYSTEM

The heart, arteries and veins make up an **organ system** in humans. The leaf and vascular tissue make up an **organ system** in plants.

leaf

leaf stalk (petiole)

phloem vessels

midrib

Surface area to volume ratio

All cells (tissues, organs, organisms) exchange gases, food and other materials with their environment. The exchanges occur mostly by diffusion across surfaces. Look at the calculations for surface area (SA), volume (V) and surface area to volume ratio (SA/V) here.

> SA of one face = 1 cm × 1 cm = 1 cm^2
> SA of cube = 1 cm^2 × 6 = 6 cm^2
> V of cube = 1 cm × 1 cm × 1 cm = 1 cm^3

a cube has 6 faces

A

$\frac{SA}{V}$ = 6:1

> SA of one face = 2 cm × 2 cm = 4 cm^2
> SA of cube = 4 cm^2 × 6 = 24 cm^2
> V of cube = 2 cm × 2 cm × 2 cm = 8 cm^3

B

$\frac{SA}{V}$ = 3:1

> SA of one face = 3 cm × 3 cm = 9 cm^2
> SA of cube = 9 cm^2 × 6 = 54 cm^2
> V of cube = 3 cm × 3 cm × 3 cm = 21 cm^3

C

$\frac{SA}{V}$ = 2:1

Cubic arithmetic

- The SA/V of cube B is half that of cube A.
- The SA/V of cube C is two-thirds that of cube B and one-third that of cube A.

Remember

The LARGER the cube becomes, the SMALLER its SA/V.

★ Surface area increases with the **square** (power^2) of the side.

★ Volume increases with the **cube** (power^3) of the side.

Cells (tissues, organs, organisms) are not cube shaped, but the calculations apply to any shape. For example, as a cell grows it

- takes in more food and gases
- produces more waste substances.

After the cell reaches a certain size, its surface area becomes too small to meet the needs of the larger volume of living matter inside.

At this point, the cell divides into two smaller daughter cells. This restores the ratio of surface area to volume because the surface area to volume ratio of a daughter cell is greater than that of the parent cell.

As a result, sufficient food and gases can pass across the cell surface into the cell.

As a result, wastes can pass across the cell surface out of the cell.

Organ systems specialised for exchanging materials

We all exchange gases, food and other materials between our body and the environment. The exchange happens slowly by diffusion across body surfaces. Different organs and organ systems are specialised to increase the available surface area for the exchange of materials with their surroundings. They make the SA/V as large as possible.

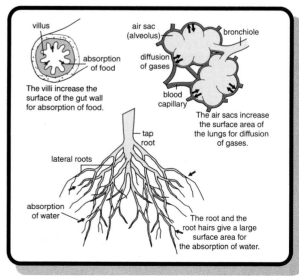

Increasing surface area

3.5 Chemicals in living things

preview

At the end of this section you will:

- understand that living things are made from the same elements as other types of matter
- know that carbohydrates, lipids, proteins and nucleic acids are important chemicals in living things
- understand that atoms of carbon are able to combine to form long chains.

Elements for life

All matter is made of chemical elements. Of these elements, six make up more than 95% by mass of living matter. They are:

- carbon (C)
- hydrogen (H)
- nitrogen (N)
- oxygen (O)
- phosphorus (P)
- sulphur (S).

The symbols of the elements arranged in order of abundance in living matter make the mnemonic **CHNOPS**.

Compounds for life

Important compounds in living things are

- **carbohydrates**: a major source of energy and structural materials
- **lipids**: stores of energy
- **proteins**: for building bodies
- **nucleic acids**: carry a code which tells cells how to make proteins.

Fact file

Carbon is the most common element in the substances that make up living things. Carbon atoms can combine to form long chains. Many of the carbon compounds in living things have large molecules (**macromolecules**) formed by small molecules combining.

Carbohydrates

Carbohydrates are compounds containing the elements carbon, hydrogen and oxygen. There are three categories:

Monosaccharides are simple sugars. Sweet-tasting **fructose** and **glucose** are examples. Both have the formula $C_6H_{12}O_6$. The six carbon atoms form a ring. Sugars (especially glucose) are an important source of energy in all living things.

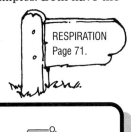

RESPIRATION Page 71.

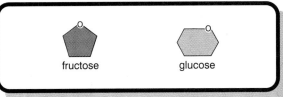

The formula of fructose and glucose in shorthand form

Disaccharides are more complex sugars. They are formed when two monosaccharides combine. For example, two molecules of glucose combine to form one molecule of **maltose**:

2 glucose → maltose + water
$$2C_6H_{12}O_6 \rightarrow C_{12}H_{22}O_{11}(aq) + H_2O$$

The formula for maltose in shorthand form

A molecule of fructose and a molecule of glucose combine to form one molecule of **sucrose**:

glucose + fructose → sucrose + water

Polysaccharides are carbohydrates whose molecules contain hundreds of sugar rings. For example, **starch**, **cellulose** and **glycogen** are polysaccharides. Their molecules consist of long chains of glucose rings.

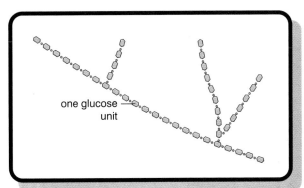

one glucose unit

Part of a starch molecule

Polysaccharides differ in the length and structure of their chains. They are important storage and structural materials in living things.

★ **Starch** is a food substance stored in plants. Their cells convert the starch into glucose, which is oxidised (respired) to release energy.

★ **Glycogen** is a food substance stored in animals. Liver cells convert glycogen into glucose, which is oxidised (respired) to release energy.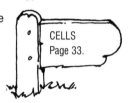

CELLS
Page 33.

★ **Cellulose** is an important component of the cell walls of plants.

★ **Chitin** is an important component of the exoskeleton of insects.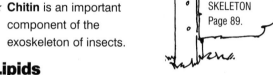

SKELETON
Page 89.

Lipids

Lipids are compounds containing the elements carbon, hydrogen and oxygen. There are two types of lipids: **fats**, which are solid at room temperature; and **oils**, which are liquid at room temperature.

Fats and oils are compounds formed between two constituents: **fatty acids** and **glycerol**. A molecule of glycerol can combine with three fatty acid molecules to form a **triglyceride** molecule and three molecules of water. Fats and oils are mixtures of triglycerides.

glycerol + fatty acid $\longrightarrow$ triglyceride + water

$$\begin{array}{c} \text{OH} \\ \text{OH} + 3\text{HA} \\ \text{OH} \end{array} \longrightarrow \begin{array}{c} \text{A} \\ \text{A} + 3\text{H}_2\text{O} \\ \text{A} \end{array}$$

Making a triglyceride

Saturated and unsaturated fats and oils

Fatty acids (and therefore the fats and oils of which they are a part) may be

- **saturated** – the carbon atoms are joined by single bonds, *or*

- **unsaturated** – the carbon atoms have double bonds between them. If there is one double bond in the molecule, the compound 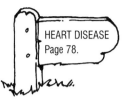 is **monounsaturated**. If there is more than one double bond in the molecule, the compound is **polyunsaturated**.

HEART DISEASE
Page 78.

Fats and oils are important as

- components of cell membranes
- sources of energy
- sources of the fat-soluble vitamins A, D and E
- insulation which helps keep the body warm
- protection for delicate organs.

Proteins

Proteins are compounds containing the elements carbon, hydrogen, oxygen, nitrogen and sometimes sulphur.

Amino acids are the building blocks which combine to make proteins. Two or more amino acids can combine to form a **peptide**, which can combine with more amino acids to form a **protein**.

Fact file

★ **Peptides** have molecules with up to 15 amino acids.

★ **Polypeptides** have molecules with 15–100 amino acids.

★ **Proteins** have still larger molecules.

There are 20 different amino acids that combine to form proteins. The protein made depends on the type and number of amino acids joining together.

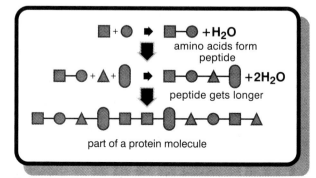

How amino acids combine to form peptides and proteins. Each shape represents a particular type of amino acid.

Proteins are important because

- they are the materials from which new tissues are made during growth and repair
- **enzymes** are proteins which control the rates of chemical reactions in cells
- **hormones** are proteins which control the activities of organisms.

HORMONES
Pages 86–7.

Enzymes in action

Enzymes are made by living cells. They are **catalysts** which control the speeds of chemical reactions in cells. There are thousands of different enzymes in a cell. Enzymes also speed up the digestion of food in the gut.

Enzymes are

- **specific** in their action – each enzyme catalyses a certain chemical reaction or type of chemical reaction

- sensitive to changes in **pH**
- sensitive to changes in **temperature**.

The substance that the enzyme helps to react is called the **substrate**. The substances formed in the reaction are called **products**.

The features of enzymes are shown below.

Nucleic acids

There are two important nucleic acids – **deoxyribonucleic acid (DNA)** and **ribonucleic acid (RNA)**.

★ DNA makes up the chromosomes in the nucleus of the cell. The **genes** that carry information from parents to offspring are lengths of DNA. They carry the **genetic code** which tells cells how to assemble amino acids in the correct order to make proteins.

★ RNA occurs in the nucleus and cytoplasm of the cell. It transfers the information in the genes to the places in the cell where proteins are made.

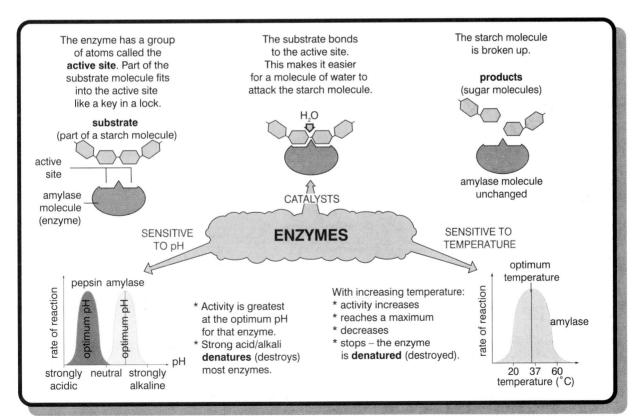

The enzyme has a group of atoms called the **active site**. Part of the substrate molecule fits into the active site like a key in a lock.

substrate
(part of a starch molecule)

active site

amylase molecule (enzyme)

The substrate bonds to the active site. This makes it easier for a molecule of water to attack the starch molecule.

H_2O

CATALYSTS

The starch molecule is broken up.

products
(sugar molecules)

amylase molecule unchanged

ENZYMES

SENSITIVE TO pH

SENSITIVE TO TEMPERATURE

pepsin amylase

rate of reaction

optimum pH   optimum pH

pH

strongly acidic   neutral   strongly alkaline

* Activity is greatest at the optimum pH for that enzyme.
* Strong acid/alkali **denatures** (destroys) most enzymes.

With increasing temperature:
* activity increases
* reaches a maximum
* decreases
* stops – the enzyme is **denatured** (destroyed).

rate of reaction

optimum temperature

amylase

20 37 60
temperature (°C)

Enzymes in action

The structure of DNA

DNA and RNA are large complex molecules made from lots of smaller molecules called **nucleotides**.

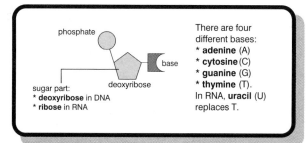

There are four different bases:
* **adenine** (A)
* **cytosine** (C)
* **guanine** (G)
* **thymine** (T).
In RNA, **uracil** (U) replaces T.

phosphate

base

sugar part:
* **deoxyribose** in DNA
* **ribose** in RNA

deoxyribose

A nucleotide molecule

★ Many nucleotides join together, sugar to phosphate, to form a long strand.

★ Two of these strands link together by **base pairing** to form a molecule of DNA.

★ The double strand twists into a spiral called a **double helix** – two intertwined spiral strands.

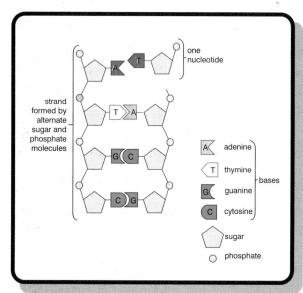

one nucleotide

strand formed by alternate sugar and phosphate molecules

A adenine
T thymine   bases
G guanine
C cytosine

sugar
phosphate

Part of a molecule of DNA

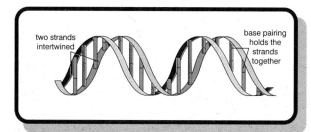

two strands intertwined

base pairing holds the strands together

The double helix: two spiral strands connected by their bases

★ A **chromosome** consists of folded strands of DNA coiled round a protein core. The DNA part of the structure controls the inheritance of characteristics.

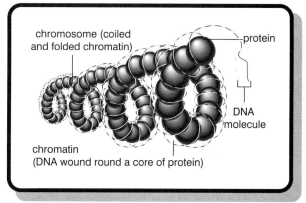

chromosome (coiled and folded chromatin)

protein

DNA molecule

chromatin
(DNA wound round a core of protein)

The structure of a chromosome

DNA replication

CELL DIVISION
Pages 38–9.

In cell division, the chromosomes **replicate** – they form an identical copy of themselves. This means the DNA molecule must make a copy of itself. The diagram below shows how this happens.

Now you can see why the daughter cells formed by mitosis are genetically identical to each other and to their parent cell. The two new molecules of DNA are each a replica of the original because of the base pairing. A always pairs with T, and G always pairs with C. All the cells in the body that die are replaced by mitosis, so they stay the same.

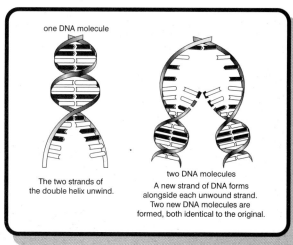

one DNA molecule

The two strands of the double helix unwind.

two DNA molecules
A new strand of DNA forms alongside each unwound strand. Two new DNA molecules are formed, both identical to the original.

DNA replication

Mutation

Hundreds of thousands of nucleotides a second can be adding to the replicating DNA. Occasionally the wrong base adds by mistake. Then the new DNA formed is slightly different from the original. The change is called a **mutation**.

The genetic code

★ A **codon** is the length of a DNA molecule that codes for one amino acid. It is three nucleotides long.

★ A **gene** is the length of a DNA molecule that codes for one complete protein.

★ So a gene is a long line of codons in a particular order.

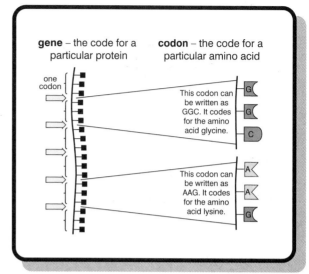

The genetic code

round-up

How much have you improved?
Work out your improvement index on page 135.

1 Which of the structures listed below are found in
a) animal cells and plant cells **b)** plant cells only?

nucleus cell membrane cell wall large vacuole mitochondria chloroplasts cytoplasm [7]

2 Describe what happens in the cells of a plant deprived of water which is then watered. How will the appearance of the plant change? [5]

3 Complete the following paragraph using the words below. Each word may be used once, more than once or not at all.

osmosis faster gains down slower partially energy against

The movement of a substance _____ a concentration gradient is called diffusion. The steeper the concentration gradient, the _____ is the rate of diffusion. Active transport occurs _____ a concentration gradient. The process requires more _____ than diffusion. The diffusion of water through a _____ permeable membrane is called _____ . [6]

4 Why is mitosis important for maintaining the health of the tissues of the body? [1]

5 Compare and contrast the processes of mitosis and meiosis by listing the similarities and the differences in different columns. [8]

6 Below is a series of words that describe the organisation of living matter. Arrange the words in the correct sequence, beginning with the simplest level of organisation and ending with the most complex.

organs cells organisms organ systems tissues [5]

7 Match each substance in column **A** with its function in column **B**.

A substances	B functions
fat	carries the genetic code
cellulose	insulates the body
DNA	a component of the plant cell wall
polypeptide	a food substance stored in the liver
glycogen	enzymes are made of this substance
protein	made of about 40 amino acids

[6]

8 a) The following is a sequence of bases for a length of DNA. How many codons are there in the sequence, assuming the first codon begins at the left-hand side and there is no overlap?

T T A G G A C T G A T C

b) If each codon codes for one amino acid, how many amino acids are coded for in this length of DNA? [2]

47

Green plants as organisms

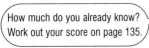

4

How much do you already know?
Work out your score on page 135.

Test yourself

1 a) Name the inorganic substances that are the raw
   materials for photosynthesis. [2]
   b) Name the gas given off during photosynthesis. [1]

2 Minerals are needed for healthy growth. Match each
   substance in column **A** with its function in column **B**.

A substances	B functions
nitrogen	used to make cell membranes
phosphorus	used to make chlorophyll
magnesium	used to make protein [3]

3 Complete the following paragraph using the words below.
   Each word may be used once, more than once or not at
   all.

   **transpiration active transport evaporation increase
   translocation osmotic stomata xylem osmosis**

   Root hairs _____ the surface area available for the
   _____ uptake of water. _____ also
   transports water across the root into the _____ .
   The uptake of minerals in solution is by _____ .
   Water moves through the _____ tissue in unbroken
   columns connecting the root with the leaves of the plant.
   Water is lost from the leaves by _____ through the
   _____ . [8]

4 Different types of tropisms are listed in column **A**. Match
   each type with the correct description in column **B**.

A tropisms	B descriptions
phototropism	growth movement in response to gravity
geotropism	growth movement in response to touch
hydrotropism	growth movement in response to light
thigmotropism	growth movement in response to water [4]

sugars — used in respiration (see page 35)
— used as building molecules to make starch which is a store of food (see pages 43–4).
— used as building molecules to make cellulose which is a component of cell walls (see pages 43–4)
— react with nitrates to form proteins (see page 44)

The uses of sugar in plants

4.1 Photosynthesis

and mineral nutrients

preview

At the end of this section you will:
- **understand that leaves are adapted for
  photosynthesis**
- **know that limiting factors affect the rate of
  photosynthesis**
- **be able to identify the minerals that plants
  need for healthy growth.**

Photosynthesis

Photosynthesis is a chemical process that traps
the energy of sunlight and uses it to convert
carbon dioxide and water into sugars. A summary
of the process is:

$$\text{carbon dioxide} + \text{water} \xrightarrow{\text{catalysed by chlorophyll}} \text{glucose} + \text{oxygen}$$

$$6CO_2(g) + 6H_2O(l) \longrightarrow C_6H_{12}O_6(aq) + 6O_2(g)$$

There are lots of different
chemical reactions that
make up the process of
photosynthesis. The
reactions happen inside

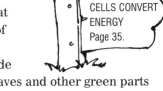

CELLS CONVERT
ENERGY
Page 35.

chloroplasts, in the leaves and other green parts
of plant cells.

Leaves

A leaf is a food-making factory. It is **adapted** for
photosynthesis.

Carbon dioxide and water
circulate within the leaf. Light is
captured by the pigment
chlorophyll, which is packaged in
the chloroplasts that pack the cells
of the leaf. On pages 50–1 is the
concept map for **photosynthesis**,
and its checklist of points. The
diagram on the left shows you how
the plant uses sugars.

Limiting factors

The rate at which plants make sugar by photosynthesis is affected by supplies of **carbon dioxide** and **water**, **temperature** and the **intensity of light**. These factors are called **limiting factors** because if any one of them falls to a low level, photosynthesis slows down or stops. The diagram below illustrates the point. At low concentrations of carbon dioxide, the carbon dioxide limits the rate of photosynthesis, whatever the light level is. Carbon dioxide is the limiting factor. At higher concentrations of carbon dioxide, the rate of photosynthesis increases if the light is bright enough. Light is now the limiting factor.

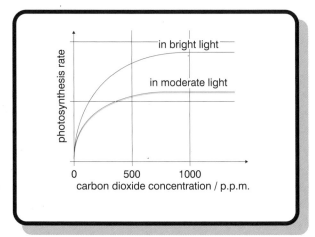

Effect of carbon dioxide concentration on the rate of photosynthesis

The higher the temperature, the faster the chemical reactions of photosynthesis, within limits. Extreme cold (below 0°C) and extreme heat (above 45°C) denature the enzymes which control the chemical reactions of photosynthesis.

Water is a raw material for photosynthesis. However, water is also the solvent in which the reactions of metabolism occur within cells. Singling out the direct effect of the availability of water on photosynthesis is therefore very difficult.

In a greenhouse, conditions are controlled so that limiting factors are eliminated.

Fact file

★ Bottles of 'plant food' sold at garden centres contain solutions of some of the important minerals needed for healthy plant growth.

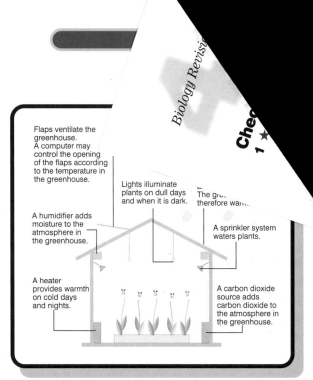

Flaps ventilate the greenhouse. A computer may control the opening of the flaps according to the temperature in the greenhouse.

Lights illuminate plants on dull days and when it is dark.

The gr... therefore wa...

A humidifier adds moisture to the atmosphere in the greenhouse.

A sprinkler system waters plants.

A heater provides warmth on cold days and nights.

A carbon dioxide source adds carbon dioxide to the atmosphere in the greenhouse.

The maximum-efficiency greenhouse

Mineral nutrients

Plants grow using the food (sugars) they make by photosynthesis. Healthy plant growth also depends on **minerals** which are absorbed from the soil through the roots as solutions of salts.

Major elements are needed in quite large amounts.

★ **Nitrogen (N)** is used by plants to make protein.

★ **Phosphorus (P)** is used by plants to make cell membranes.

★ **Potassium (K)** is needed for photosynthesis.

Plants deprived of any of the major elements grow less well. Most artificial fertilisers are NPK fertilisers.

Trace elements (micronutrients) are needed in much smaller amounts than major elements.

★ **Magnesium (Mg)** is a component of the chlorophyll molecule.

★ **Iron (Fe)** is also a component of the chlorophyll molecule.

If magnesium and iron are in short supply then leaves become mottled and pale. **Copper (Cu)**, **sodium (Na)** and **manganese (Mn)** are also trace elements. Absence of any one of them from the soil leads to poor plant growth.

...cklist for photosynthesis

Leaves are arranged so that the lower ones are not overshadowed by those above. The arrangement is called the **leaf mosaic**.

As a result, more leaves are exposed to direct sunlight.

★ The leaf blade is flat.

As a result, a large surface area is exposed for the absorption of light.

★ The leaf blade is thin.

As a result, light reaches the lower layers of cells in the leaf.

2 ★ Water moves up to leaves in the **transpiration stream**.

★ Carbon dioxide enters leaves through the **stomata**.

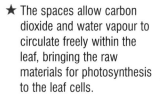
TRANSPIRATION
Pages 52–5.

3 ★ The cells of the upper leaf surface do not contain chloroplasts and are transparent.

★ **Palisade cells** beneath the upper epidermis are column shaped, tightly packed and filled with chloroplasts.

As a result, many chloroplasts are exposed to bright light, maximising the rate of photosynthesis.

★ **Spongy mesophyll cells** contain fewer chloroplasts and are more loosely packed.

As a result, there are air spaces between the spongy mesophyll cells.

★ The spaces allow carbon dioxide and water vapour to circulate freely within the leaf, bringing the raw materials for photosynthesis to the leaf cells.

STOMATA
Page 52.

★ Each **stoma** is flanked by guard cells which control the size of the opening of the stoma.

As a result, the rate of diffusion of gases into and out of the leaf through the stomata is controlled.

★ The cells of the lower leaf surface lack chloroplasts, except the guard cells.

4 ★ Chloroplasts pack the inside of each palisade cell.

★ Chloroplasts stream in the cytoplasm (**cyclosis**) to the region of the palisade cell where light is brightest.

As a result, the rate of photosynthesis is maximised.

5 ★ Membranes inside the chloroplasts are covered with the green pigment **chlorophyll**.

★ Chlorophyll absorbs light, especially wavelengths in the red and blue parts of the spectrum.

★ The membranes are arranged like stacks of pancakes, maximising the surface area of chlorophyll exposed to light.

6 ★ During photosynthesis, light energy is converted into the energy of chemical bonds of glucose (sugar).

★ Chlorophyll makes light energy available for the synthesis (making) of sugar.

★ The region between membranes contains enzymes which convert water and carbon dioxide into sugar. The energy needed for conversion comes from the light absorbed by chlorophyll.

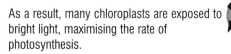
membrane of chloroplast

PHOTOSYNTHESIS IN ACTION
Water molecules and carbon dioxide molecules combine to form sugar. The chemical reactions produce oxygen.

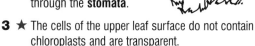

carbon dioxide + water ⟶ sugar + oxygen

INSIDE THE CHLOROPLAST

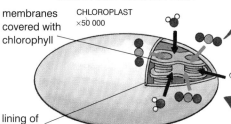

membranes covered with chlorophyll

CHLOROPLAST ×50 000

lining of chloroplast cut away

Track the route of water molecules and carbon dioxide molecules into the chloroplast.

CHECK 6 LIST

CHECK 5 LIST

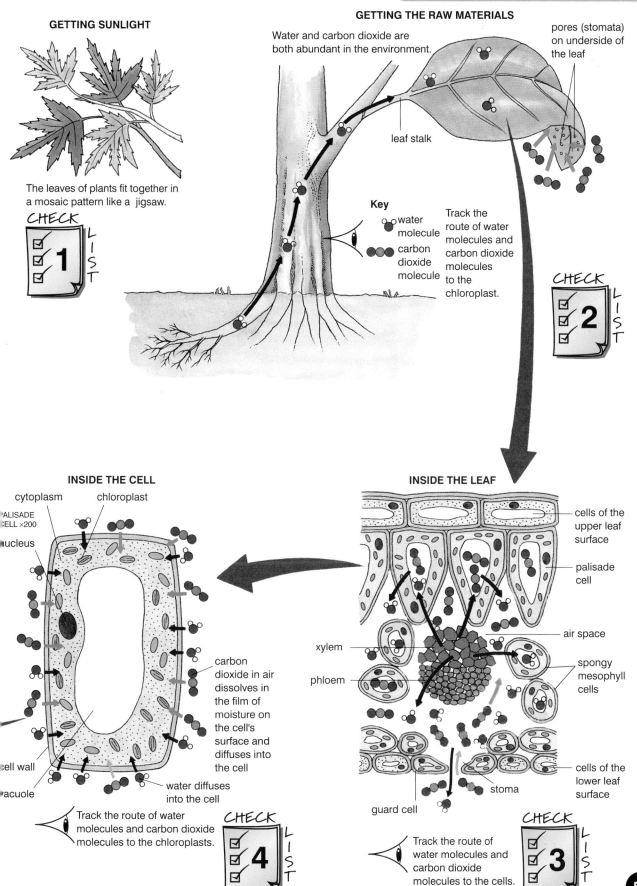

GETTING SUNLIGHT

The leaves of plants fit together in a mosaic pattern like a jigsaw.

CHECK **1** LIST
☑ ☑ ☑

GETTING THE RAW MATERIALS

Water and carbon dioxide are both abundant in the environment.

pores (stomata) on underside of the leaf

leaf stalk

Key
○● water molecule
●●● carbon dioxide molecule

Track the route of water molecules and carbon dioxide molecules to the chloroplast.

CHECK **2** LIST
☑ ☑ ☑

INSIDE THE CELL

cytoplasm chloroplast

PALISADE CELL ×200

nucleus

cell wall

vacuole

carbon dioxide in air dissolves in the film of moisture on the cell's surface and diffuses into the cell

water diffuses into the cell

Track the route of water molecules and carbon dioxide molecules to the chloroplasts.

CHECK **4** LIST
☑ ☑ ☑

INSIDE THE LEAF

cells of the upper leaf surface

palisade cell

air space

spongy mesophyll cells

xylem

phloem

cells of the lower leaf surface

stoma

guard cell

Track the route of water molecules and carbon dioxide molecules to the cells.

CHECK **3** LIST
☑ ☑ ☑

51

4.2 Transport in plants

preview

At the end of this section you will:
- **know that xylem tissue transports water and that phloem tissue transports food**
- **understand the processes of transpiration and translocation**
- **know that xylem tissue and phloem tissue form vascular bundles which reach all parts of the plant.**

Transport systems in plants

On pages 54–5 is the concept map for **transport in plants**, and its checklist. Study them carefully.

Factors affecting transpiration

Think of the ways plants lose and gain water.

★ Loss of water is through transpiration.

★ Gain is through the uptake of water by the roots.

If the loss of water is greater than the gain, then the stomata close.

As a result, transpiration is reduced.

If the loss of water is still more than the gain, then the cells of the plant lose turgor and the plant **wilts**.

The graphs show the effect of other factors on the rate of transpiration. Light stimulates the stomata to open wide. The rate of transpiration is therefore greater during the day than at night.

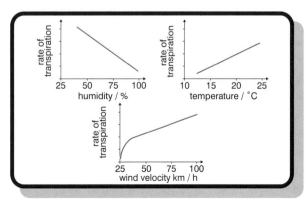

Factors affecting the rate of transpiration

Controlling the size of stomata

Two sausage-shaped **guard cells** surround the opening which forms the stoma. The guard cells contain chloroplasts. Think of the sequence:

★ During the day, photosynthesis increases the concentration of sugar in the guard cells. There is a net flow of water by osmosis into the guard cells making them turgid. The guard cells bow out, opening the stoma.

★ At night, photosynthesis stops and the concentration of sugar in the guard cells falls. There is a net outflow of water and the guard cells lose turgor. The guard cells bow in, closing the stoma.

4.3 Plant responses

preview

At the end of this section you will know that:
- **plants grow in response to stimuli**
- **there are two sorts of growth movement – nastic movements and tropic movements (tropisms)**
- **plant hormones (growth substances) affect the growth of plants**
- **auxin is an example of a plant hormone**
- **commercial applications of plant hormones include weed control and the production of 'seedless' fruits.**

Nastys and tropisms

Plants move by growing in response to stimuli. One part of the plant grows faster than another. There are two types of growth movement.

FACTS

★ **Nastic movements** are responses to stimuli that come from all directions. For example, flowers open and close in response to changes in temperature.

★ **Tropic movements** (tropisms) are responses to stimuli which come mainly from one direction. For example, shoots bend towards light.

How plants respond

The diagram below and its checklist are your revision guide to **plant responses**. Study them carefully.

Checklist for plant responses

1 ★ Tropisms are **positive** if the plant grows towards the stimulus and **negative** if it grows away.

As a result of different positive and negative tropisms, the different parts of the plant grow in a way that increases the plant's chances of survival. For example, the roots 'find' water, leaves receive as much light as possible for photosynthesis.

★ The growing tips (shoot/root) of a plant are receptors for different stimuli.

2 ★ Auxin makes the cellulose wall of plant cells more elastic.

As a result, the cells elongate rapidly.

As a result, the cells on the shady side of the shoot tip grow *more* rapidly than the cells on the brightly lit side.

As a result, the shoot tip bends towards the light.

3 ★ The effect of the hormone produced by the root cap is different from auxin produced by the shoot tip. It *slows down* growth in the underside of the root tip.

As a result, the root bends down.

Fact file

★ The stems of some types of plant respond to the touch of an object by growing in a spiral around the object. The response is called thigmotropism. Sweet peas and runner beans show thigmotropism. They spiral round canes stuck into the ground to support them.

★ Does it matter which way up a seed is planted? Positive phototropism means that the shoot will always grow upwards. Positive geotropism means that the roots will always grow downwards. So no matter which way up a seed is, its shoot and roots will always grow in the right direction.

★ Auxin sometimes prevents growth. It diffuses down the stem and prevents the growth of side shoots. Lopping the top off a plant removes the source of auxin and side branches then develop. This is why a gardener trims a hedge to make it more bushy.

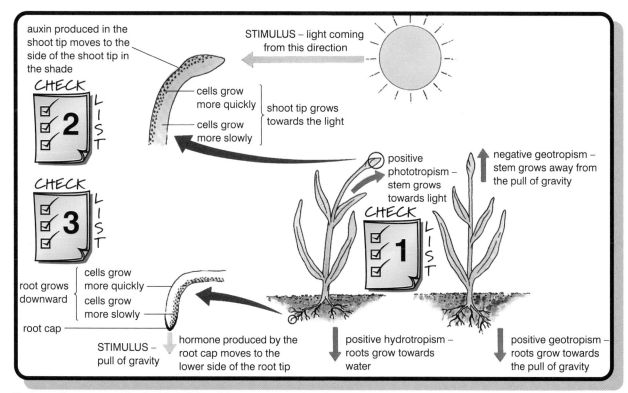

Tropisms – the response of the shoot tip to light and the root cap to gravity and water

TRANSPORT OF FOOD

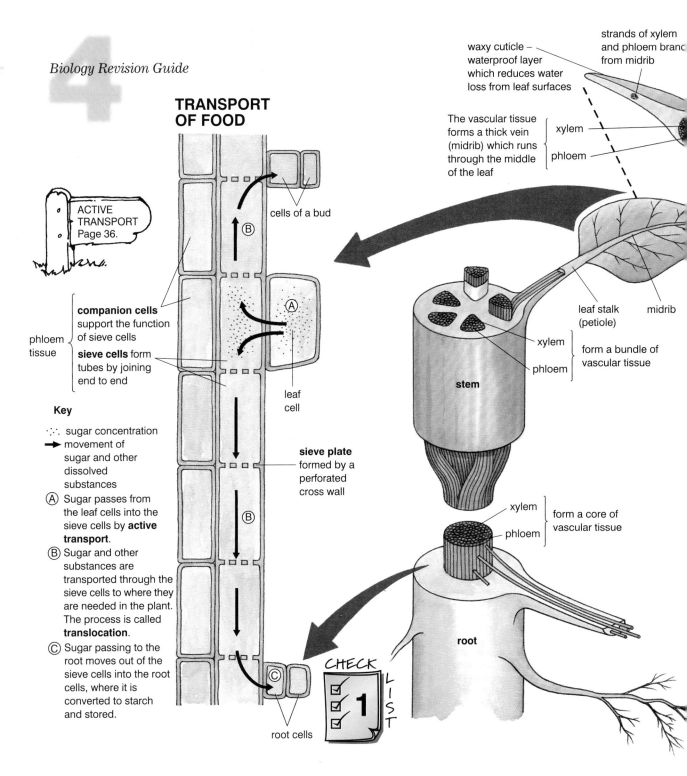

ACTIVE TRANSPORT Page 36.

cells of a bud

Ⓑ

Ⓐ

companion cells support the function of sieve cells

phloem tissue

sieve cells form tubes by joining end to end

leaf cell

Key

∴ sugar concentration

→ movement of sugar and other dissolved substances

Ⓐ Sugar passes from the leaf cells into the sieve cells by **active transport**.

Ⓑ Sugar and other substances are transported through the sieve cells to where they are needed in the plant. The process is called **translocation**.

Ⓒ Sugar passing to the root moves out of the sieve cells into the root cells, where it is converted to starch and stored.

sieve plate formed by a perforated cross wall

Ⓑ

Ⓒ

CHECK LIST ☑☑☑ **1**

root cells

waxy cuticle – waterproof layer which reduces water loss from leaf surfaces

strands of xylem and phloem branc from midrib

The vascular tissue forms a thick vein (midrib) which runs through the middle of the leaf

xylem

phloem

leaf stalk (petiole)

midrib

stem

xylem

phloem

form a bundle of vascular tissue

xylem

phloem

form a core of vascular tissue

root

TRANSPORT OF WATER

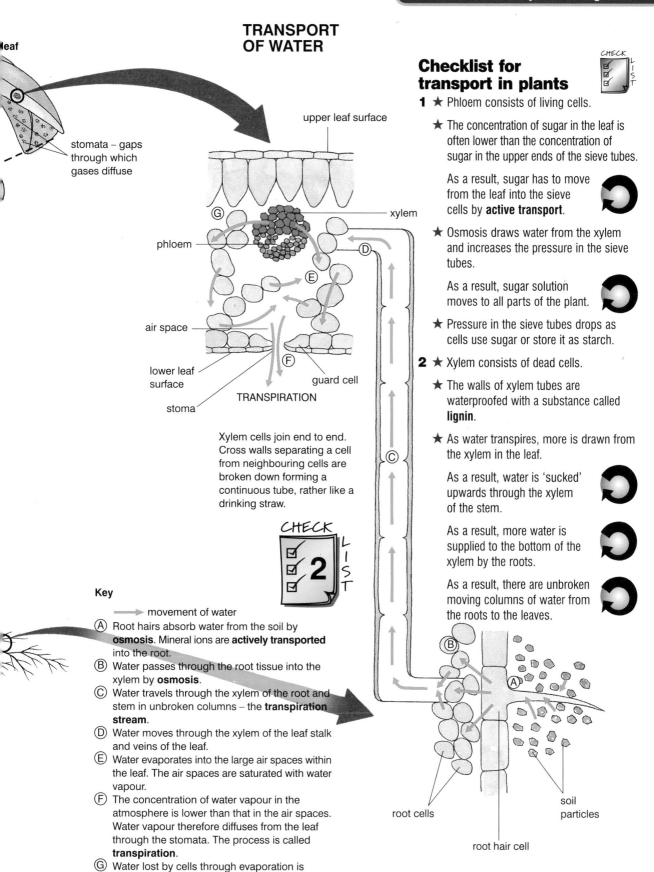

leaf

stomata – gaps through which gases diffuse

upper leaf surface

xylem

G

phloem

D

E

air space

lower leaf surface

F

stoma

guard cell

TRANSPIRATION

Xylem cells join end to end. Cross walls separating a cell from neighbouring cells are broken down forming a continuous tube, rather like a drinking straw.

CHECK LIST 2

C

B

A

root cells

soil particles

root hair cell

Key

→ movement of water

Ⓐ Root hairs absorb water from the soil by **osmosis**. Mineral ions are **actively transported** into the root.

Ⓑ Water passes through the root tissue into the xylem by **osmosis**.

Ⓒ Water travels through the xylem of the root and stem in unbroken columns – the **transpiration stream**.

Ⓓ Water moves through the xylem of the leaf stalk and veins of the leaf.

Ⓔ Water evaporates into the large air spaces within the leaf. The air spaces are saturated with water vapour.

Ⓕ The concentration of water vapour in the atmosphere is lower than that in the air spaces. Water vapour therefore diffuses from the leaf through the stomata. The process is called **transpiration**.

Ⓖ Water lost by cells through evaporation is replaced with water drawn through the cells by osmosis. Cells next to the xylem draw water from the xylem by osmosis.

Checklist for transport in plants

CHECK LIST

1 ★ Phloem consists of living cells.

★ The concentration of sugar in the leaf is often lower than the concentration of sugar in the upper ends of the sieve tubes.

As a result, sugar has to move from the leaf into the sieve cells by **active transport**.

★ Osmosis draws water from the xylem and increases the pressure in the sieve tubes.

As a result, sugar solution moves to all parts of the plant.

★ Pressure in the sieve tubes drops as cells use sugar or store it as starch.

2 ★ Xylem consists of dead cells.

★ The walls of xylem tubes are waterproofed with a substance called **lignin**.

★ As water transpires, more is drawn from the xylem in the leaf.

As a result, water is 'sucked' upwards through the xylem of the stem.

As a result, more water is supplied to the bottom of the xylem by the roots.

As a result, there are unbroken moving columns of water from the roots to the leaves.

The shoot tip

The diagram below shows the sorts of experiments carried out by scientists investigating the response of plants to light. These experiments suggest that there is a growth substance (auxin) which

- is produced in the shoot tip
- diffuses to the region behind the shoot tip
- stimulates growth so that the shoot bends towards light.

Using plant hormones

★ **Ripening** – fruit is quickly ripened in sheds in an atmosphere which contains one part of **ethene** per million parts of air.

★ **Weedkillers** – 2,4-D (2,4-dichlorophenoxyethanoic acid) is a synthetic auxin which kills plants by making them grow too fast. Broad-leaved weed plants like docks, daisies and dandelions are more sensitive to 2,4-D than narrow-leaved crop plants like wheat and barley.

★ **Seedless fruit** – an auxin paste smeared over the carpels of some crop species produces fruit without fertilisation. Seedless cucumbers and seedless tomatoes are produced in this way.

★ **Rooting** – gardeners use 'rooting powder' which contains auxin to encourage root growth from stem cuttings.

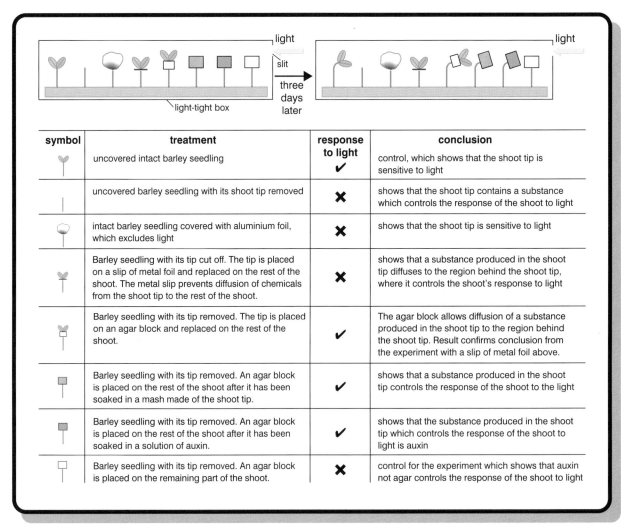

symbol	treatment	response to light	conclusion
	uncovered intact barley seedling	✔	control, which shows that the shoot tip is sensitive to light
	uncovered barley seedling with its shoot tip removed	✘	shows that the shoot tip contains a substance which controls the response of the shoot to light
	intact barley seedling covered with aluminium foil, which excludes light	✘	shows that the shoot tip is sensitive to light
	Barley seedling with its tip cut off. The tip is placed on a slip of metal foil and replaced on the rest of the shoot. The metal slip prevents diffusion of chemicals from the shoot tip to the rest of the shoot.	✘	shows that a substance produced in the shoot tip diffuses to the region behind the shoot tip, where it controls the shoot's response to light
	Barley seedling with its tip removed. The tip is placed on an agar block and replaced on the rest of the shoot.	✔	The agar block allows diffusion of a substance produced in the shoot tip to the region behind the shoot tip. Result confirms conclusion from the experiment with a slip of metal foil above.
	Barley seedling with its tip removed. An agar block is placed on the rest of the shoot after it has been soaked in a mash made of the shoot tip.	✔	shows that a substance produced in the shoot tip controls the response of the shoot to the light
	Barley seedling with its tip removed. An agar block is placed on the rest of the shoot after it has been soaked in a solution of auxin.	✔	shows that the substance produced in the shoot tip which controls the response of the shoot to light is auxin
	Barley seedling with its tip removed. An agar block is placed on the remaining part of the shoot.	✘	control for the experiment which shows that auxin not agar controls the response of the shoot to light

Response of the shoot tip to light

round-up

How much have you improved?
Work out your improvement index on pages 135–6.

1 Name the different cells in the leaf that contain chloroplasts. [3]

2 Briefly explain why most chloroplasts are found in palisade cells lying just beneath the upper surface of the leaf. [4]

3 List the major limiting factors for photosynthesis. Briefly explain how a greenhouse overcomes the effect of limiting factors on the growth of plants. [8]

4 Complete the following paragraph using the words below. Each word may be used once, more than once or not at all.

**xylem transport sugar translocation
transpiration phloem pressure
active transport water**

Leaves produce _____ by photosynthesis. The concentration of _____ in leaf cells is often less than that in nearby _____ tissue. _____ therefore moves from the leaf cell into the _____ by _____ . Osmosis draws _____ into the _____ tissue increasing _____ which helps transport sugar. The transport of sugar is called _____ . Storage of _____ as starch in the root cells reduces _____ in the _____ . [13]

5 Describe the probable climate on a day when the transpiration rate of a plant is at a maximum. [4]

6 Briefly explain what happens if a plant loses more water through transpiration than it gains through absorption of water by its roots. [3]

7 Compare the characteristics of xylem tissue with those of phloem tissue. List the comparisons in two columns headed 'xylem' and 'phloem' respectively. [5]

8 Complete the following paragraph using the words below. Each word may be used once, more than once or not at all.

**weedkiller ripens plant hormone
unfertilised tip seedless slowly**

Auxin is a _____ produced in the _____ of the shoot. Synthetic auxin is used as a _____ to kill unwanted plants. Auxin paste applied to the _____ carpels of some crop species produces _____ fruits. Fruit stored in an atmosphere containing ethene _____ more quickly. [6]

9 The diagram shows an experiment on the shoots of growing seedlings. In experiment A a thin piece of metal was placed between the tip of the shoot and the rest of the stem. In experiment B a thin piece of metal was placed further down, separating the shoot into an upper part and a lower part.

A   B

The growing seedlings were placed in a box which was light-tight except for a slit on one side. The seedlings were illuminated for three days.

a) What hypothesis was the scientist trying to test? [2]

b) In each case, what do you think the response of the seedling will be to the light source? (Assume the seedlings survived the treatment for the time of the experiment.) [2]

Explain your answer. [4]

Well done if you've improved. Don't worry if you haven't. Take a break and try again.

Humans as organisms

How much do you already know?
Work out your score on page 136.

Test yourself

1 The nutrients in food are listed below. Use these nutrients to answer the following questions.

carbohydrates fats proteins vitamins minerals

a) Which nutrients give food its energy content? [3]
b) Which nutrient is a source of energy, but is most important in the body for growth and repair? [1]
c) Which nutrient releases the most energy per gram? [1]
d) Which nutrients are needed only in small amounts, but play an important role in the control of metabolism? [2]

2 Match each term in column **A** with its correct description in column **B**.

A terms	B descriptions
ingestion	the removal of undigested food through the anus
digestion	digested food passes into the body
absorption	food is taken into the mouth
egestion	food is broken down [4]

3 Explain the differences between
a) bronchi and bronchioles [2]
b) lungs and alveoli [2]
c) aerobic respiration and anaerobic respiration [4]
d) breathing and gaseous exchange. [3]

4 Explain how the heart functions as a double pump. [4]

5 The different components of blood are listed in column **A**. Match each component with its correct description in column **B**.

A components	B descriptions
plasma	contain haemoglobin
red blood cells	promote the formation of blood clots
white blood cells	contains dissolved food substances
platelets	produce antibodies [4]

6 The components of the reflex arc are listed as follows: sensory neurone, effector, relay neurone, receptor, motor neurone. Write the components in their correct order. [4]

7 What is the function of each of these parts of the ear?
a) the eardrum   b) the bones of the middle ear
c) the pinna   d) the hair cells [8]

8 What are hormones and how are they transported around the body? [2]

9 Distinguish between the roles of the hormones insulin and glucagon in keeping the blood glucose level steady. [2]

10 The structures of the kidney tubule and its blood supply are listed below. Rewrite them in the order in which a molecule of urea passes from the renal artery to the outside of the body.

**tubule urethra bladder glomerulus
Bowman's capsule ureter collecting duct** [7]

11 How are the teeth of a dog adapted for grasping and cutting food? [4]

12 The mussel is a bivalve (two shells) mollusc. Briefly explain how a mussel filters food from the water in which it lives. [6]

13 Match the different types of skeleton in column **A** with their correct description in column **B**.

A skeletons	B descriptions
endoskeleton	the skeleton is a body space filled with fluid
exoskeleton	the skeleton lies inside the body
hydrostatic skeleton	the skeleton surrounds the body [3]

5.1 Food and diet

preview

At the end of this section you will:
● **understand that different foods contain different amounts of energy**
● **be able to identify the components of a diet**
● **know the role of different foods in the body.**

Nutrients in food

The **nutrients** in food are **carbohydrates**, **fats**, **proteins**, **vitamins** and **minerals**. **Water** and **fibre** are also components of food. Different foods contain nutrients, water and fibre in different proportions. Our **diet** is the food and drink we take in. Remember the sequence:

$$\left.\begin{array}{l}\text{nutrient}\\+\text{ water}\\+\text{ fibre}\end{array}\right\}\xrightarrow{\text{components of}}\text{food}\xrightarrow{\text{eaten}}\text{diet}$$

All living things (including us) need food. The nutrients in food are a source of

- **energy** which powers life's activities
- materials for the **growth** and **repair** of bodies
- substances which control the **metabolism** of cells.

On pages 60–1 is a Mind Map for **food and diet**. The checklist of points gives you more information.

Checklist for food and diet

1 ★ The **energy value** of food is measured using an instrument called a bomb calorimeter, shown below.

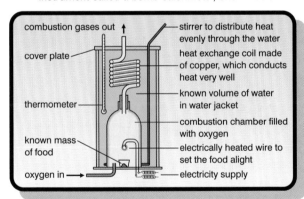

combustion gases out ↑
cover plate
thermometer
known mass of food
oxygen in →

stirrer to distribute heat evenly through the water
heat exchange coil made of copper, which conducts heat very well
known volume of water in water jacket
combustion chamber filled with oxygen
electrically heated wire to set the food alight
electricity supply

A bomb calorimeter

The burning food heats the surrounding water. The change in temperature of the water is used to work out the energy value of the food:

$$\text{energy released per gram}=\frac{\text{volume of water in water jacket}\times\text{temperature rise}}{\text{mass of food}}\times 4.2$$

★ The energy released from food depends on the nutrients it contains.
- 17.2 kJ/g for carbohydrate
- 22.2 kJ/g for protein
- 38.5 kJ/g for fat

Although protein is an 'energy nutrient', its most important use in the body is for growth and repair.

★ People have different energy requirements depending on their
- **age** – on average young people have greater energy requirements than older people
- **gender** (male or female) – pregnancy and lactation (milk production) increase the energy requirements of women
- **activities** – any kind of activity increases a person's energy requirements.

★ The rate at which the body uses energy is called the **metabolic rate**. It is lowest (called the **basal metabolic rate**) when the body is at rest.

★ If a person eats more food than is necessary for his/her energy needs, the excess is turned into fat.

As a result, the person puts on weight.

★ To lose weight, a person can
- take more exercise, which increases energy output
- eat less high-energy food, decreasing energy input.

2 ★ **Additives** are put into food to
- make it tastier
- make it more attractive
- improve its texture
- prevent it from spoiling.

★ Some additives can make some people unwell.

3 ★ A **balanced diet** is a mixture of foods which together provide sufficient nutrients for healthy living.

★ The 'basic four' food groups help us choose a balanced diet.

4 ★ The amount of **alcohol** people consume is measured in units, as shown below.

unit of alcohol	one measure of whisky	one glass of sherry	one glass of table wine	half a pint of beer or lager
1 =	=	=	=	

Units of alcohol

★ How much alcohol is too much? It depends on a person's age, size, gender (male or female) and metabolic rate.

5 ★ Vitamin C helps cells to join together. It also controls the use of calcium by bones and teeth.

★ Vitamin D helps the body to absorb calcium.

★ Deficiency of iron is a common cause of anaemia.

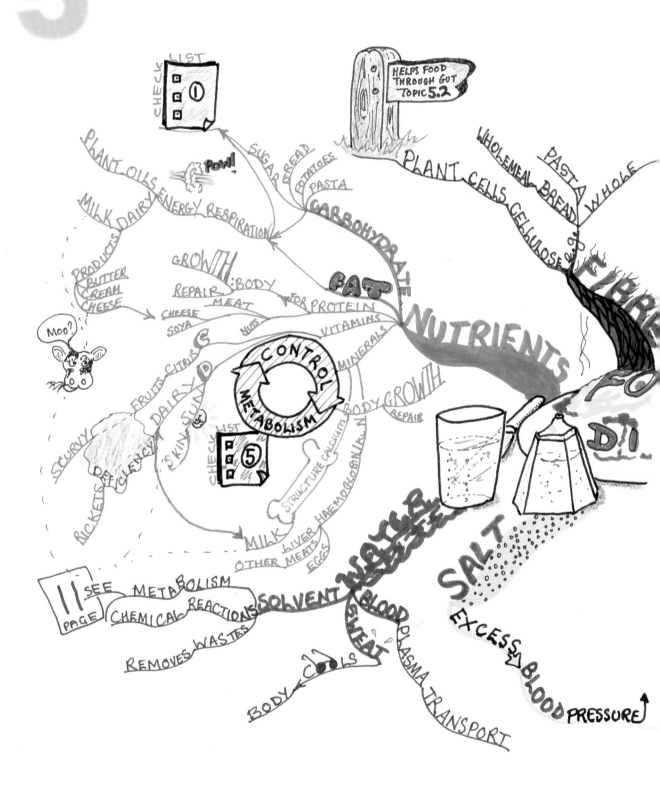

CHECK LIST ☑ ☑ ☑ ①

POW!

HELPS FOOD THROUGH GUT TOPIC 5.2

PLANT CELLS CELLULOSE

WHOLEMEAL BREAD PASTA WHOLE

FIBRE

FO

PLANT OILS ENERGY RESPIRATION

SUGAR BREAD POTATOES PASTA

CARBOHYDRATE

MILK DAIRY

PRODUCTS BUTTER CREAM CHEESE

Moo?

GROWTH REPAIR :BODY MEAT CHEESE SOYA NUTS

FOR PROTEIN

FAT

VITAMINS MINERALS

NUTRIENTS

DI

CONTROL METABOLISM

FRUITS CITRUS C

DAIRY D

SUN

SCURVY SKIN

BODY GROWTH REPAIR

CHECK LIST ☐ ☐ ☐ ⑤

DEFICIENCY

STRUCTURE CALCIUM

BONE HAEMOGLOBIN IRON

RICKETS

MILK LIVER OTHER MEATS EGGS

WATER

SALT

II PAGE SEE METABOLISM CHEMICAL REACTIONS REMOVES WASTES

SOLVENT BLOOD PLASMA

SWEAT

EXCESS BLOOD PRESSURE

BODY COOLS TRANSPORT

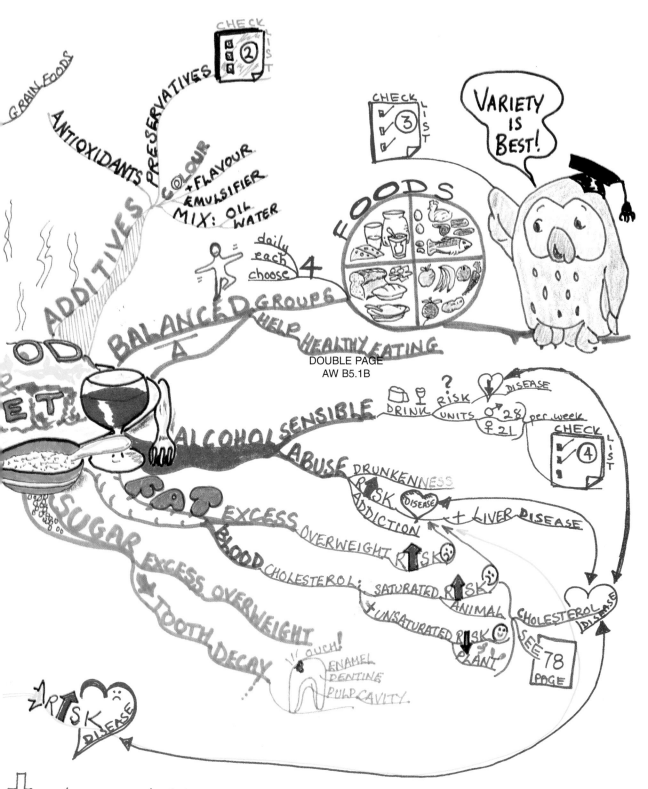

DOUBLE PAGE
AW B5.1B

⇩ = decreased risk

⇧ = increased risk

5

5.2 The digestive system
preview

At the end of this section you will:

- **know that the digestive system is a muscular tube through which food moves**
- **understand that as food moves through the digestive system it is processed (digested) into substances which the cells of the body can absorb and use**
- **be able to identify enzymes responsible for digesting food**
- **know that digestive systems are adapted to type of diet.**

Testing your understanding

The terms:

gut
intestine } all refer to the digestive system.
alimentary canal

Digesting food

Food is processed through the digestive system in the following sequence:

ingestion
food is taken
into the mouth

↓

digestion
large molecules of
food are broken down
into smaller molecules

↓

absorption
the small molecules
of digested food
pass into the body

↓

egestion
undigested food is
removed from the body
through the anus

The digestive system is a muscular tube through which food moves. It processes food.

★ **Mechanical processes** break up food and mix it with digestive juices.

★ **Chemical processes** digest food using different enzymes in the digestive juices. The body cannot absorb the large molecules of carbohydrate, protein and fat in food. They are broken down into smaller molecules which the body can absorb.

On pages 64–5 is the concept map for **the digestive system**. The **liver** and **pancreas** are connected by ducts to the digestive system. They play an important role in the digestion of food. The numbers on the concept map refer to the checklist below.

Checklist for the digestive system

(M) = mechanical processes of digestion

(C) = chemical processes of digestion

1 ★ **(M) Teeth** chew food, breaking it into small pieces.

As a result, the surface area of food exposed to the action of digestive enzymes is increased.

As a result, food is digested more quickly.

2 ★ **(C) Saliva**, produced by the salivary glands, contains the enzyme **amylase**.

As a result, the digestion of starch begins in the mouth.

★ **(M)** Saliva moistens the food.

As a result, the food is made slippery for easy swallowing.

3 ★ **(M)** Muscles of the **stomach** wall and **small intestine** mix food thoroughly with different juices containing digestive enzymes.

As a result, a liquid paste called **chyme** is formed.

As a result, food and digestive enzymes are brought into intimate contact.

★ **(C)** Gastric juice, produced by **pits** in the stomach wall, contains **hydrochloric acid** and the enzymes **pepsin** and **renin**.

Hydrochloric acid
- increases the acidity of the stomach contents.

As a result, bacteria in the food are killed.

As a result, the action of salivary amylase is stopped.

Pepsin
- begins the digestion of protein.

Renin
- clots milk, making it semi-solid.

As a result, milk stays in the gut long enough to be digested.

4 ★ **(C) Bile**, produced by the **liver**, is a green alkaline liquid which is stored in the gall bladder before release into the small intestine through the bile duct. It
- neutralises acid from the stomach
- breaks fat into small droplets (**emulsification**).

As a result, the surface area of fat exposed to the action of the enzyme **lipase** is increased.

As a result, fat is digested more quickly.

5 ★ **(C) Pancreatic juice**, produced by the **pancreas**, is released into the small intestine through the pancreatic duct. It contains
- **sodium carbonate** which neutralises stomach acid
- **carbohydrases**, **proteases** and **lipases** (see table below) which digest carbohydrate, protein and fat.

6 ★ **(C) Intestinal juice**, produced by glands in the wall of the **duodenum** and **ileum**, contains
- **carbohydrases** and **lipases** that complete the digestion of carbohydrates and fats.

Chemistry of digestion

Digestive enzymes catalyse the breakdown of food by **hydrolysis**. Water splits large molecules of food into smaller molecules which are suitable for absorption into the body. The table below summarises the process.

What happens to digested food?

Digested food is carried away from the ileum in the blood of the hepatic portal vein and in the fluid of the lymph vessels.

★ Blood transports water, sugars, glycerol and amino acids to the liver.

★ Lymph transports fats and fat-soluble vitamins to a vein in the neck where the substances enter the bloodstream.

VEINS Page 74.
LYMPH VESSELS Page 75.

The **liver** plays a major role in the metabolism of food substances after they have been absorbed into the body.

★ Glucose may be converted to **glycogen** and stored in the liver. Glycogen may be hydrolysed to glucose and released back into the blood in response to the body's needs.

★ Iron, obtained from destroyed red blood cells, is stored in the liver.

★ Amino acids in excess of the body's needs are broken down (a process called **deamination**) in the liver. Urea is formed and excreted in urine.

★ Amino acids are converted from one type into another in the liver (a process called **transamination**) according to the body's needs.

enzyme group	example	where found	food component	after digestion
carbohydrases (catalyse the digestion of carbohydrates)	amylase	mouth	starch	maltose
	maltase	small intestine	maltose	glucose
proteases (catalyse the digestion of proteins)	pepsin	stomach	protein	polypeptides
	chymotrypsin dipeptidase	small intestine	polypeptides dipeptides	dipeptides amino acids
lipases (catalyse the digestion of fats)	lipase	small intestine	fat	fatty acids + glycerol

Enzymes that digest carbohydrates, proteins and fats

MOVING FOOD (throughout the gut)

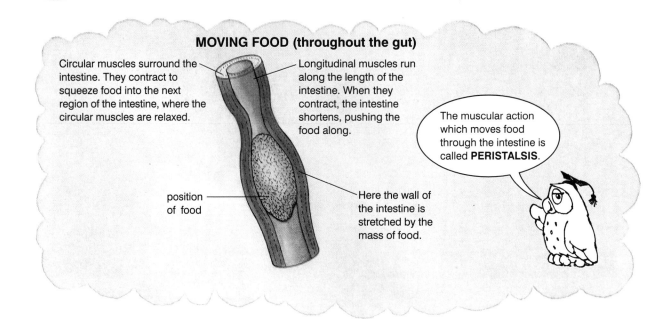

Circular muscles surround the intestine. They contract to squeeze food into the next region of the intestine, where the circular muscles are relaxed.

Longitudinal muscles run along the length of the intestine. When they contract, the intestine shortens, pushing the food along.

The muscular action which moves food through the intestine is called **PERISTALSIS**.

position of food

Here the wall of the intestine is stretched by the mass of food.

ABSORPTION (ileum and colon)

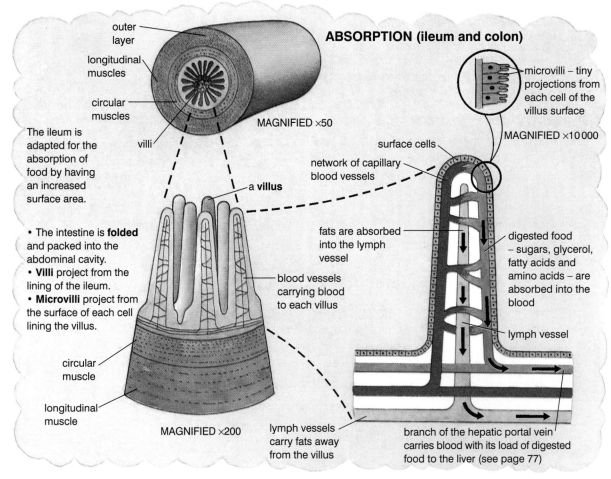

outer layer

longitudinal muscles

circular muscles

villi

MAGNIFIED ×50

microvilli – tiny projections from each cell of the villus surface

MAGNIFIED ×10 000

The ileum is adapted for the absorption of food by having an increased surface area.

• The intestine is **folded** and packed into the abdominal cavity.
• **Villi** project from the lining of the ileum.
• **Microvilli** project from the surface of each cell lining the villus.

a **villus**

surface cells

network of capillary blood vessels

fats are absorbed into the lymph vessel

blood vessels carrying blood to each villus

digested food – sugars, glycerol, fatty acids and amino acids – are absorbed into the blood

lymph vessel

circular muscle

longitudinal muscle

MAGNIFIED ×200

lymph vessels carry fats away from the villus

branch of the hepatic portal vein carries blood with its load of digested food to the liver (see page 77)

The digestive system – its structure and functions (checklist on pages 62–3)

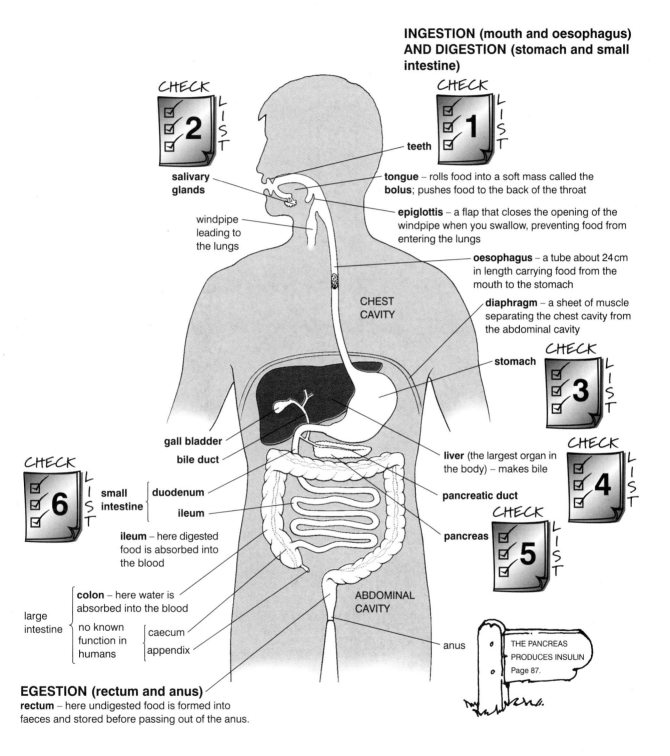

INGESTION (mouth and oesophagus) AND DIGESTION (stomach and small intestine)

CHECK **2** LIST

CHECK **1** LIST

teeth

tongue – rolls food into a soft mass called the **bolus**; pushes food to the back of the throat

salivary glands

epiglottis – a flap that closes the opening of the windpipe when you swallow, preventing food from entering the lungs

windpipe leading to the lungs

oesophagus – a tube about 24 cm in length carrying food from the mouth to the stomach

CHEST CAVITY

diaphragm – a sheet of muscle separating the chest cavity from the abdominal cavity

stomach

CHECK **3** LIST

gall bladder

bile duct

liver (the largest organ in the body) – makes bile

CHECK **4** LIST

CHECK **6** LIST

small intestine { **duodenum**

ileum

pancreatic duct

CHECK **5** LIST

pancreas

ileum – here digested food is absorbed into the blood

colon – here water is absorbed into the blood

large intestine {

no known function in humans

caecum

appendix

ABDOMINAL CAVITY

anus

THE PANCREAS PRODUCES INSULIN
Page 87.

EGESTION (rectum and anus)
rectum – here undigested food is formed into faeces and stored before passing out of the anus.

Digestive system and diet

Remember that:

★ Omnivores eat both plants and meat.

★ Herbivores eat plants.

★ Carnivores eat meat.

FOOD CHAINS
AND WEBS
Pages 18–19.

Most humans are omnivores, and the human digestive system is adapted to deal with a mixture of plant and animal foods. Rabbits and cattle are herbivorous, with digestive systems adapted to deal with plant food; cats are carnivorous with a digestive system adapted for meat.

Fact file

★ Most animals do not produce enzymes (called cellulases) to digest the cellulose in the walls of plant cells. Different species of bacteria and protist do produce cellulases.

Cattle have a large stomach in four parts. The **rumen** and **reticulum** receive the food first. The rumen contains microorganisms which produce cellulases that digest the cellulose in the plant material. Here the food forms into balls of **cud** which return to the mouth where they are thoroughly re-chewed before being re-swallowed. Animals that chew cud are called **ruminants**. The **omasum** and **abomasum** receive the cud and protein digestion then takes place.

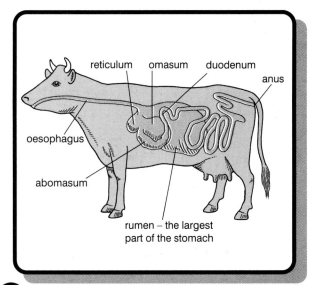

Rabbits do not chew cud. Instead they eat the pellets of faeces produced from the food's first journey through the gut.

• Pellets are soft and contain a lot of undigested food.

As a result, microorganisms which live in the **appendix** have another chance of dealing with the food second time through. Faecal pellets produced after the food's second journey through are hard.

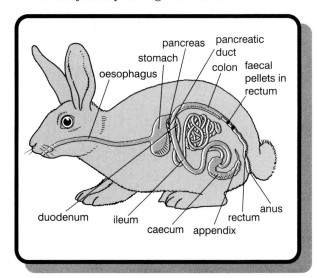

Cats do not chew their food. Having caught it, they swallow it whole or in large chunks. The stomach is large so that it can store the meal while it is digested bit by bit.

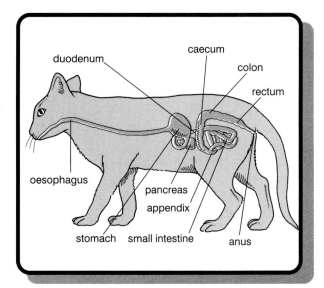

5.3 Obtaining food

preview

At the end of this section you will:
- **be able to distinguish between filter feeders and fluid feeders**
- **know the structure of a tooth**
- **understand the arrangement of teeth in the mouth**
- **be able to identify adaptations of the skull and teeth to different diets.**

When animals take in (**ingest**) food, we say that they are **feeding**. Different animals have different structures for feeding.

Filter feeders

Animals that feed by straining food from the water in which they live are called **filter feeders**. Bivalve (two-shelled) molluscs and whales are examples of filter feeders.

Mussels are bivalve molluscs. They live in shallow water near the sea-shore. The mussel attaches itself to rocks and stones by a muscular **foot**. Two shells close round the animal. The diagram at the top of the next column shows the shells prized open and the arrangement of body parts within. The **gills** are covered with beating cilia which draw a current of water containing microscopic organisms between the shells. The mussel filters the microscopic organisms from the water by trapping them in mucus that covers the mantle and gills. The mucus and entrapped food are then drawn into the mouth.

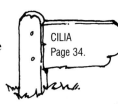

CILIA
Page 34.

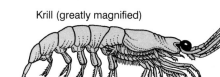

Krill (greatly magnified)

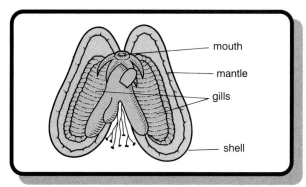

Inside a mussel

Baleen whales like the blue whale feed on the minute protists that form the dense plankton layer at the ocean's surface.

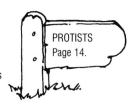

PROTISTS
Page 14.

The blue whale also feeds on huge quantities of tiny shrimps called **krill**, filtered from the water. The diagram below shows how the water is strained through a series of horny plates (called **baleen**) that grow down from the sides of the upper jaw. The shrimps are caught in the bristles of the baleen plates and then swallowed.

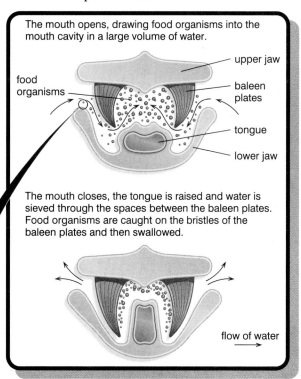

The mouth opens, drawing food organisms into the mouth cavity in a large volume of water.

food organisms — upper jaw — baleen plates — tongue — lower jaw

The mouth closes, the tongue is raised and water is sieved through the spaces between the baleen plates. Food organisms are caught on the bristles of the baleen plates and then swallowed.

flow of water

Cross-section through the head of a baleen whale

Fluid feeders

Insects feed on the fluids of animals or plants in different ways. They may

- suck fluids directly
- pierce tissues and then suck the fluids in them
- suck food which is first liquefied by enzymes in the insect's saliva.

The diagram on the opposite page shows examples of the categories of insect fluid feeders.

Teeth

Teeth are the feeding structures of most vertebrates except birds.

VERTEBRATES
Page 12.

The diagram below shows the internal structure of a human tooth.

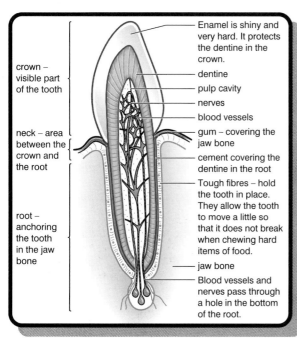

crown – visible part of the tooth

Enamel is shiny and very hard. It protects the dentine in the crown.

dentine

pulp cavity

nerves

blood vessels

gum – covering the jaw bone

neck – area between the crown and the root

cement covering the dentine in the root

Tough fibres – hold the tooth in place. They allow the tooth to move a little so that it does not break when chewing hard items of food.

root – anchoring the tooth in the jaw bone

jaw bone

Blood vessels and nerves pass through a hole in the bottom of the root.

Structure of a human tooth

Types of teeth

Mammals deal with food in different ways, and their teeth are adapted accordingly.

★ **Incisors** are chisel shaped for biting and cutting food.

★ **Canines** are pointed for piercing, slashing and tearing food.

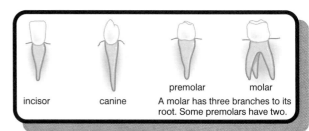

incisor   canine   premolar   molar

A molar has three branches to its root. Some premolars have two.

The four basic types of human teeth

★ **Premolars** and **molars** are large, with broad surfaces made uneven by bumps called **cusps**, for crushing and grinding food.

The different types of teeth are positioned in the mouth according to their function. The word **dentition** is used to describe the number and arrangement of teeth in an animal.

Tooth enamel is the hardest substance in the body. It consists of calcium salts bound together by the protein **keratin**.

Omnivore dentition

Humans and other omnivores have all four basic types of teeth. The dentition is described in a **dental formula** using the letters shown here.

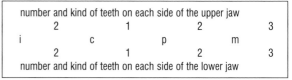

number and kind of teeth on each side of the upper jaw							
	2		1		2		3
i		c		p		m	
	2		1		2		3
number and kind of teeth on each side of the lower jaw							

Human dental formula

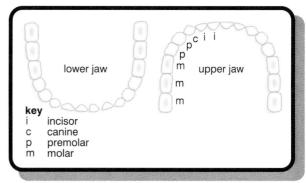

lower jaw

c i i
p
p
m   upper jaw
m
m

key
i   incisor
c   canine
p   premolar
m   molar

The arrangement of teeth in the adult human jaw

Aphids pierce plant tissues and suck the fluids in them. The aphid inserts its hollow needle-like mouthparts (stylets) through the surface of a plant stem into a sieve tube (see page 54). Sap, under pressure in the sieve tubes, is forced through the mouthparts and into the aphid gut.

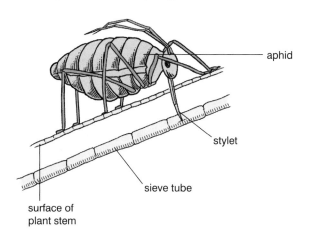

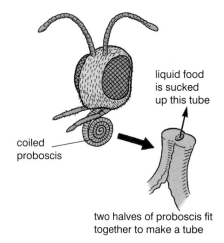

Butterflies suck nectar from flowers.
The mouthparts are in the form of a long **proboscis**. Grooves along each half of the proboscis fit together to make a tube. The tip of the proboscis is placed in the nectar which is sucked up the tube like water up a drinking straw. When the proboscis is not in use, it is coiled up like a clock spring.

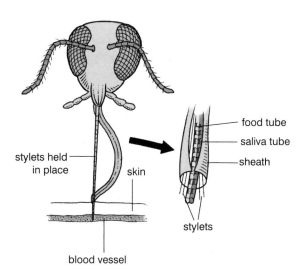

Houseflies first liquefy food externally and then suck it up. The mouthparts of the housefly form a proboscis which has a two-lobed pad at its tip. In the pad are many thin tubes. During feeding, saliva is pumped down these tubes onto the food. Enzymes in saliva liquefy the food. The liquid food is then sucked up the tubes and into the mouth.

Mosquitoes pierce animal tissues and suck the fluids in them. Female mosquitoes feed on blood. Their mouthparts are long and sharply pointed, forming stylets surrounded by a sheath-like structure. Inside are a food tube and a tube through which saliva passes. The stylets pierce the victim's skin until a blood vessel is reached. The food tube is then pushed in and saliva pumped down through the salivary tube into the wound. Chemicals in the saliva stop the blood clotting as it is sucked up into the mouth.

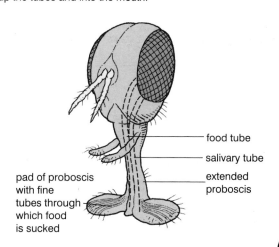

Insect fluid feeders

There are 32 teeth in total in the adult human jaw. In children there are 24 teeth, 20 of which have been gradually replaced by the permanent teeth by the age of about twelve. The teeth in children are called **milk teeth**. The third molars of the permanent teeth are called the **wisdom teeth** and do not appear until the age of about 20.

Herbivore dentition

The dentition of sheep and cattle is adapted to

- sweep grass into the mouth with the tongue poking through the **diastema** (gap between the canines and premolars)
- cut off the grass by the lower incisors nipping against the pad in the upper jaw
- grind the grass between the ridged, broad surfaces of the premolars and molars. The joint of the jaw moves from side to side as well as up and down which makes grinding food easier.

number and kind of teeth on each side of the upper jaw				
0		0	3	3
i	c	p	m	
3	1	3	3	
number and kind of teeth on each side of the lower jaw				

Sheep dental formula

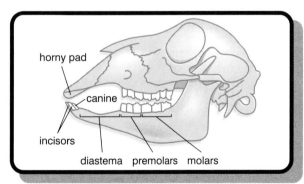

The arrangement of teeth in the jaws of a sheep. Notice that there are no canines in the upper jaw, and the canines in the lower jaw look like incisors.

Carnivore dentition

The dental formula of dogs shows that their dentition is adapted to

- catch, hold and tear struggling prey with long, well developed canines
- cut through flesh and bone with incisors, premolars and molars.

Powerful jaw muscles ensure a firm grip and bite. The jaw joint only allows up-and-down movements.

number and kind of teeth on each side of the upper jaw				
3		1	4	2
i	c	p	m	
3	1	4	3	
number and kind of teeth on each side of the lower jaw				

Dog dental formula

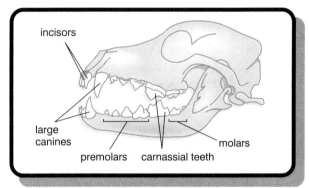

The arrangement of teeth in the jaws of a dog. Notice that the last premolar on each side of the upper jaw and the first molar on each side of the lower jaw are fused to form the large **carnassial teeth**. They work like scissors, cutting through flesh and bone.

Looking after your teeth

Sugary food is especially bad for your teeth. It encourages bacteria to multiply and form **plaque** on the surfaces of the teeth.

★ The bacteria break down sugar in the mouth to form acids.
★ The acids soften the enamel which begins the process of decay (called **dental caries**).
★ The decay penetrates the layer of dentine, eventually reaching the pulp cavity.

The result is the agony of toothache. The pain is caused by nerves in the pulp cavity responding when decay penetrates the tooth.

Owl's routine for helping to prevent tooth decay

★ *Reduce* the amount of sugary food in your diet.
★ *Clean* your teeth regularly with a toothbrush – at least after breakfast and last thing at night.
★ *Floss* between your teeth where the toothbrush cannot reach.
★ *Visit* the dentist for a check-up every six months.

5.4 Breathing, gaseous exchange and respiration

preview

At the end of this section you will:

- **know that breathing in (inhalation) takes air into the lungs and that breathing out (exhalation) pushes air out from the lungs**
- **be able to describe how breathing movements take place**
- **know that the exchange of gases (oxygen and carbon dioxide) happens in the lungs, between the air sacs (alveoli) and the capillary blood vessels**
- **understand that the blood transports oxygen to cells which use it for aerobic respiration**
- **be able to distinguish between aerobic respiration and anaerobic respiration.**

Respiration

Remember the distinction between respiration and gaseous exchange. Oxygen is used by cells to oxidise digested food substances (glucose) to release energy. The process is called **aerobic respiration**. The energy released from the oxidation of glucose powers the activities which define the characteristics of life. The table shows that there is less oxygen in exhaled air than in inhaled air. This is because some of the oxygen is used by cells for aerobic respiration. There is more carbon dioxide in exhaled air than in inhaled air because carbon dioxide is produced by the chemical reactions of aerobic respiration.

gas	amount in inhaled air / %	amount in exhaled air / %
nitrogen	78	78
oxygen	21	16
noble gases	1	1
carbon dioxide	0.03	4
water vapour	0	1

Differences between inhaled and exhaled air

★ How does oxygen reach cells?

★ How does carbon dioxide leave cells?

The answer is by gaseous exchange.

Now you can see the link between breathing air, gaseous exchange and aerobic respiration.

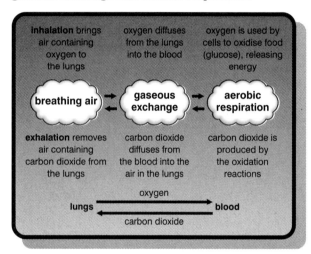

On page 72 is the concept map for **breathing, gaseous exchange and respiration**. The numbers on the concept map refer to the checklist below.

Checklist for breathing, gaseous exchange and respiration

1 ★ The **upper respiratory tract** is a tube from the nostrils and mouth to the lungs.
   - It is well supplied with blood.

   As a result, inhaled air is warmed to body temperature.

   - Hairs in the nasal passage filter out large dust particles.
   - The lining of **mucus** traps bacteria, viruses and dust particles.
   - Hair-like **cilia** sweep the mucus into the **pharynx**, where it is either swallowed, sneezed out or coughed up.

   As a result, the air entering the lungs is cleaned and freed of disease-causing microorganisms.

2 ★ The network of **bronchioles** in the lungs form the **bronchial tree**.

   ★ The millions of **alveoli** in a pair of human lungs form a surface area of about 90 m².

   As a result, gaseous exchange is very efficient.

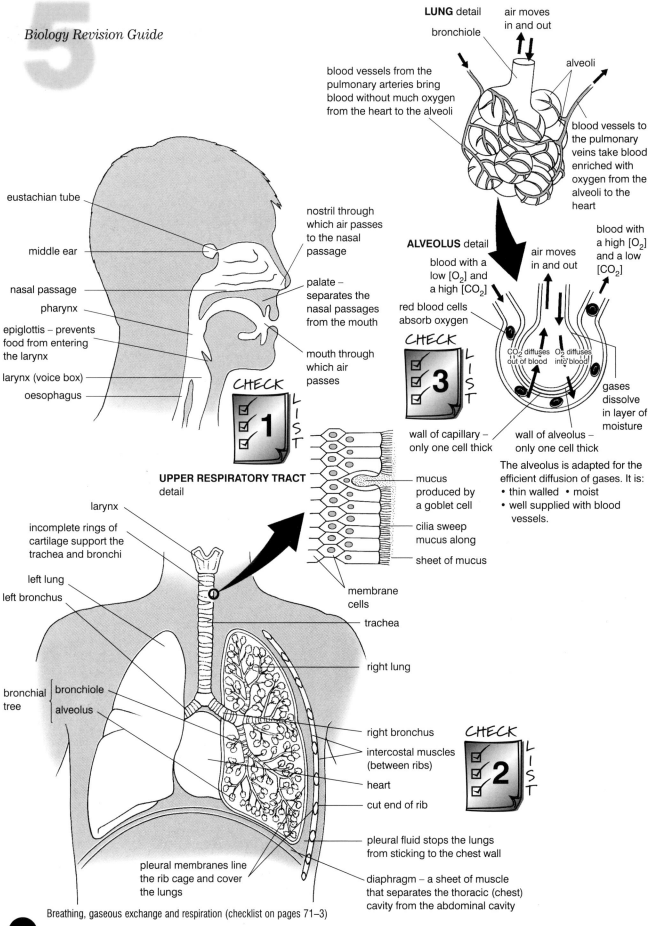

LUNG detail

air moves in and out

bronchiole

alveoli

blood vessels from the pulmonary arteries bring blood without much oxygen from the heart to the alveoli

blood vessels to the pulmonary veins take blood enriched with oxygen from the alveoli to the heart

eustachian tube

middle ear

nasal passage

pharynx

epiglottis – prevents food from entering the larynx

larynx (voice box)

oesophagus

nostril through which air passes to the nasal passage

palate – separates the nasal passages from the mouth

mouth through which air passes

ALVEOLUS detail

air moves in and out

blood with a high $[O_2]$ and a low $[CO_2]$

blood with a low $[O_2]$ and a high $[CO_2]$

red blood cells absorb oxygen

CO_2 diffuses out of blood

O_2 diffuses into blood

gases dissolve in layer of moisture

wall of capillary – only one cell thick

wall of alveolus – only one cell thick

The alveolus is adapted for the efficient diffusion of gases. It is:
• thin walled • moist
• well supplied with blood vessels.

CHECK 1 LIST

CHECK 3 LIST

UPPER RESPIRATORY TRACT detail

mucus produced by a goblet cell

cilia sweep mucus along

sheet of mucus

membrane cells

larynx

incomplete rings of cartilage support the trachea and bronchi

left lung

left bronchus

bronchial tree { bronchiole, alveolus

trachea

right lung

right bronchus

intercostal muscles (between ribs)

heart

cut end of rib

pleural fluid stops the lungs from sticking to the chest wall

diaphragm – a sheet of muscle that separates the thoracic (chest) cavity from the abdominal cavity

CHECK 2 LIST

pleural membranes line the rib cage and cover the lungs

Breathing, gaseous exchange and respiration (checklist on pages 71–3)

3 ★ The chemical reactions of aerobic respiration take place inside the mitochondria of cells.

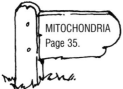

MITOCHONDRIA Page 35.

★ Cells do not use the energy from aerobic respiration as soon as it is released. It is converted into the energy of chemical bonds in a substance called **adenosine triphosphate** (**ATP**). ATP is the link between the cell's energy-releasing activities and its energy-using activities.

Breathing movements

The **ribs** and **diaphragm** form an elastic cage around the lungs. As they move, the pressure in the lungs changes. This change in pressure causes **inhaling** (breathing in) and **exhaling** (breathing out).

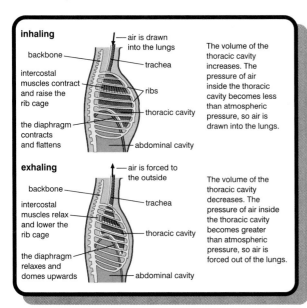

inhaling

air is drawn into the lungs

backbone

intercostal muscles contract and raise the rib cage

trachea

ribs

the diaphragm contracts and flattens

thoracic cavity

abdominal cavity

The volume of the thoracic cavity increases. The pressure of air inside the thoracic cavity becomes less than atmospheric pressure, so air is drawn into the lungs.

exhaling

air is forced to the outside

backbone

intercostal muscles relax and lower the rib cage

trachea

the diaphragm relaxes and domes upwards

thoracic cavity

abdominal cavity

The volume of the thoracic cavity decreases. The pressure of air inside the thoracic cavity becomes greater than atmospheric pressure, so air is forced out of the lungs.

Inhaling and exhaling

Remember

★ **All** cells respire – animal cells, plant cells and the cells of fungi and single-celled organisms.

★ **Most** cells respire aerobically.

★ **Some** cells, such as muscle cells, the cells of plant roots, yeast cells and some types of bacteria, are able to respire anaerobically when supplies of oxygen are low.

★ **Some** cells, such as the bacterium that causes tetanus, can *only* respire anaerobically.

Mutual friends!

The muscles of the man and dog are working hard. At first, aerobic respiration in their muscle cells gives them a flying start.

glucose + oxygen → carbon dioxide + water

$$C_6H_{12}O_6(aq) + 6O_2(g) \rightarrow 6CO_2(g) + 6H_2O(l)$$

energy released = 16.1 kJ/g glucose

The man and dog are both panting. However, in spite of rapid breathing and strenuous pumping by the heart, oxygen cannot reach the muscles fast enough to supply their needs.

The muscles then switch from aerobic respiration to **anaerobic respiration** which does *not* use oxygen. **Lactic acid** is produced, which collects in the muscles.

$$\begin{array}{cc} \text{glucose} & \rightarrow \quad \text{lactic acid} \\ C_6H_{12}O_6(aq) & 2CH_3CHOHCO_2H(aq) \end{array}$$

energy released = 0.83 kJ/g glucose

Notice that the energy released per gram of glucose is less than in aerobic respiration. As lactic acid accumulates, the muscles stop working. The man and dog will be unable to run any further until the lactic acid has been removed from their muscles. This removal process uses oxygen. Lactic acid stimulates the body to pant vigorously, bringing a rush of oxygen to the muscles. During the recovery period, the lactic acid is oxidised and the **oxygen debt** is repaid. Aerobic respiration can then start again.

The chemical reactions of anaerobic respiration provide us with food, drink and a range of other products – see Chapter 8.

5.5 Blood and the circulatory system

preview

At the end of this section you will:
- be able to identify the different components of blood
- understand the functions of blood
- understand why the heart is a double pump
- know that capillary blood vessels link arteries and veins
- understand how different factors (diet, exercise and stress) affect the circulatory system.

Fact file

★ The **heart** is a pump.

★ **Blood** is a liquid containing different cells.

★ **Arteries, veins** and **capillaries** are tube-like vessels through which blood flows.

$$\text{heart} \xrightarrow{\text{pumps}} \text{blood} \xrightarrow{\text{through}} \text{blood vessels}$$

Moving blood around

The circulatory system consists of tubes (arteries, veins and capillaries) through which blood is pumped by the heart. Blood carries oxygen, digested food, hormones and other substances *to* the tissues and organs of the body that need them. Blood also carries carbon dioxide and other waste substances produced by the metabolism of cells *from* the tissues and organs of the body. On pages 76–7 is the concept map for **blood and the circulatory system**. The numbers on the concept map refer to the checklist below.

Checklist for blood and the circulatory system

1 ★ **Red blood cells** are made in the **marrow** of the limb bones, ribs and vertebrae.

★ Old red blood cells are destroyed in the liver.

LIVER
Page 63.

★ **White blood cells** originate in the **bone marrow** and **spleen**.

★ **Antibodies** produced against a particular **antigen** will attack only that antigen. The antibody is said to be **specific** to that antigen.

2 ★ **Arteries** carry blood *from* the heart.

Veins carry blood *to* the heart.

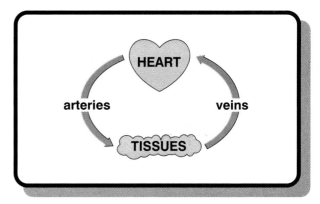

3 ★ Heart (**cardiac**) muscle contracts and relaxes rhythmically for a lifetime.

★ **Valves** direct the flow of blood through the heart.

★ The heartbeat is a two-tone sound:
- **diastole** – the heart muscles are relaxed
- **systole** – the heart muscles contract. During **auricular systole**, contraction of the auricles (atria) forces blood into the ventricles. During **ventricular systole**, contraction of the ventricles forces blood into the pulmonary artery (from the right ventricle) and aorta (from the left ventricle)

★ The heart is a **double pump**.

★ The beating of the heart is controlled by a **pacemaker**.

As a result, the heart beats on average 72 times a minute.

4 ★ The arteries and veins in the human body form two circuits:
- the lung circuit
- the head and body circuit.

Testing your understanding

Examinations test your understanding of ideas and important principles. Be sure you have grasped the arrangement of the **hepatic portal vein** and the role of the **pulmonary artery** and **pulmonary vein**.

Understanding the hepatic portal vein

Veins carry blood to the heart. The **hepatic portal vein** is the exception. Notice on page 77 that it carries blood with its load of digested food from the intestine to the liver.

ABSORPTION OF FOOD Page 64.

Understanding the pulmonary artery and the pulmonary vein

Arteries are often described as carriers of oxygenated blood (often coloured red on diagrams), and veins as carriers of deoxygenated blood (often coloured blue on diagrams). However, the **pulmonary artery** carries deoxygenated blood from the heart to the lungs. The **pulmonary vein** carries oxygenated blood from the lungs to the heart.

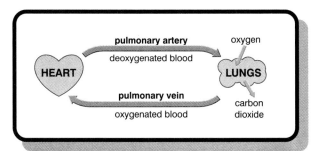

Capillaries – fact file

Capillaries are tiny blood vessels, 0.001 mm in diameter.

★ The walls of capillary blood vessels are one cell thick.

As a result, substances easily diffuse between blood in the capillaries and the surrounding tissues.

★ Capillaries form dense networks called **beds** in the tissues of the body.

As a result, no cell is very far away from a capillary.

★ The blood in capillaries supplies nearby cells with oxygen, food molecules and other substances. It also carries away carbon dioxide and other wastes produced by the cells' metabolism.

★ **Tissue fluid** carries oxygen, food and other substances to the cells. This fluid is blood plasma that has been forced out through the thin capillary walls by the pressure of the blood inside.

★ Red blood cells squeeze through the smallest capillaries in single file.

As a result, the pressure drops as blood passes through the capillaries from the artery to the vein.

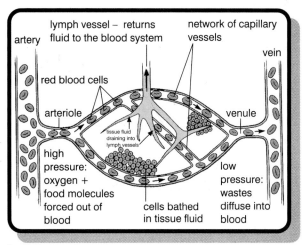

Capillaries at work

Disorders of the blood

★ **Leukaemia** is the overproduction of abnormal white blood cells.

As a result, there are too few red blood cells.

Treatment is with drugs that slow the production of white blood cells, and radiotherapy which kills the abnormal cells.

★ **Haemophilia** is a genetic disease which runs in families. The blood does not clot properly because factor VIII, one of the substances in the blood needed for blood clots to form, is missing.

As a result, **haemophiliacs** (people suffering from haemophilia) lose a lot of blood if they injure themselves.

Treatment is by injections of factor VIII.

GENETIC DISEASES Page 99.

BLOOD

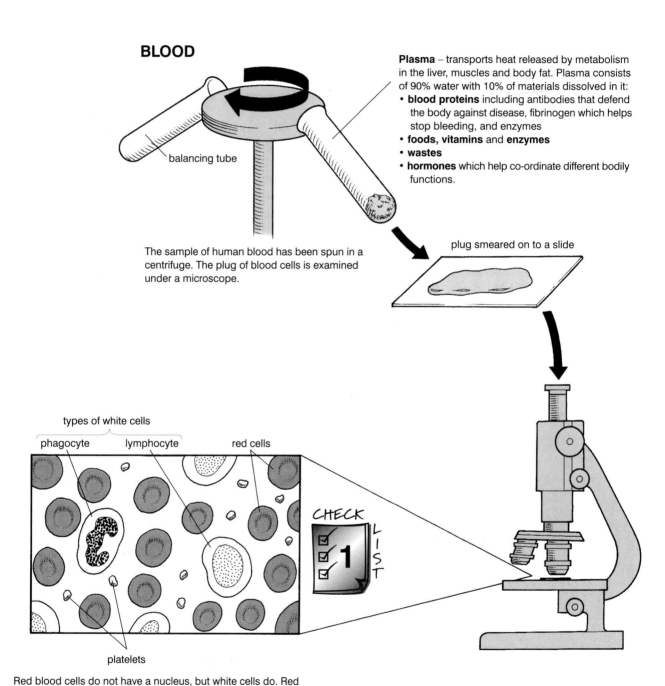

Plasma – transports heat released by metabolism in the liver, muscles and body fat. Plasma consists of 90% water with 10% of materials dissolved in it:
- **blood proteins** including antibodies that defend the body against disease, fibrinogen which helps stop bleeding, and enzymes
- **foods, vitamins** and **enzymes**
- **wastes**
- **hormones** which help co-ordinate different bodily functions.

balancing tube

The sample of human blood has been spun in a centrifuge. The plug of blood cells is examined under a microscope.

plug smeared on to a slide

types of white cells

phagocyte   lymphocyte   red cells

CHECK
LIST
1

platelets

Red blood cells do not have a nucleus, but white cells do. Red cells are packed with the pigment haemoglobin which gives cells their red colour. Notice the characteristic shapes of the nuclei of phagocytes and lymphocytes. Platelets look like fragments of red cells.

Blood and the circulatory system (checklist on page 74)

BLOOD SYSTEM

HEAD
oxygen goes to tissues from blood: carbon dioxide and wastes go to blood from tissues

jugular vein carries blood from head to heart

carotid artery carries blood from heart to head

LUNGS
oxygen goes to blood: carbon dioxide goes from blood

pulmonary artery carries blood to the lungs from the heart

HEART

aorta from which arteries branch to the organs and tissues of the body

right atrium

vena cavae into which veins drain blood from the head and body

valves

left atrium

valves

right ventricle

left ventricle

LIVER
food stored: wastes changed to urea: oxygen goes to tissues from blood: carbon dioxide and urea go to blood from tissues

hepatic portal vein brings blood rich in digested food from the intestine to the liver

BODY   **INTESTINE**
food absorbed into blood: oxygen goes to tissues from blood: carbon dioxide and wastes go to blood from tissues

KIDNEYS
urea removed: oxygen goes to tissues from blood: carbon dioxide and wastes go to blood from tissues

BODY MUSCLES
oxygen goes to tissues from blood: carbon dioxide and wastes go to blood from tissues

→ direction of blood flow

VALVES

pen valve

Valves ensure that blood flows in one direction only. Inside the veins, where blood is at a lower pressure than in the arteries, valves stop blood flowing backwards.

wall of vein

vein squeezed by body muscles

queezing by body muscles moves blood up through the vein

wall of vein

valve

losed valve

Enlarged cut-away diagram showing pocket-like valves set in the wall of vein. If blood flows back, it fills the pockets closing the valve

BLOOD VESSELS

ARTERIES

thick outer wall

thick layer of muscles and elastic fibres withstand pressure of blood

narrow diameter

smooth lining

• carry blood away from the heart to organs and tissues
• blood at high pressure
• have a pulse because the vessel walls expand and relax as blood spurts from the heart

VEINS

fairly thin outer wall

thin layer of muscles and elastic fibres easily expand reducing resistance to the flow of blood returning to the heart

smooth lining

large diameter

• return blood to the heart from organs and tissues (except hepatic portal vein)
• blood at low pressure
• working body muscles squeeze the veins, helping push blood to the heart
• do not have a pulse since blood flows smoothly
• have valves

CHECK **4** LIST

CHECK **3** LIST

CHECK **2** LIST

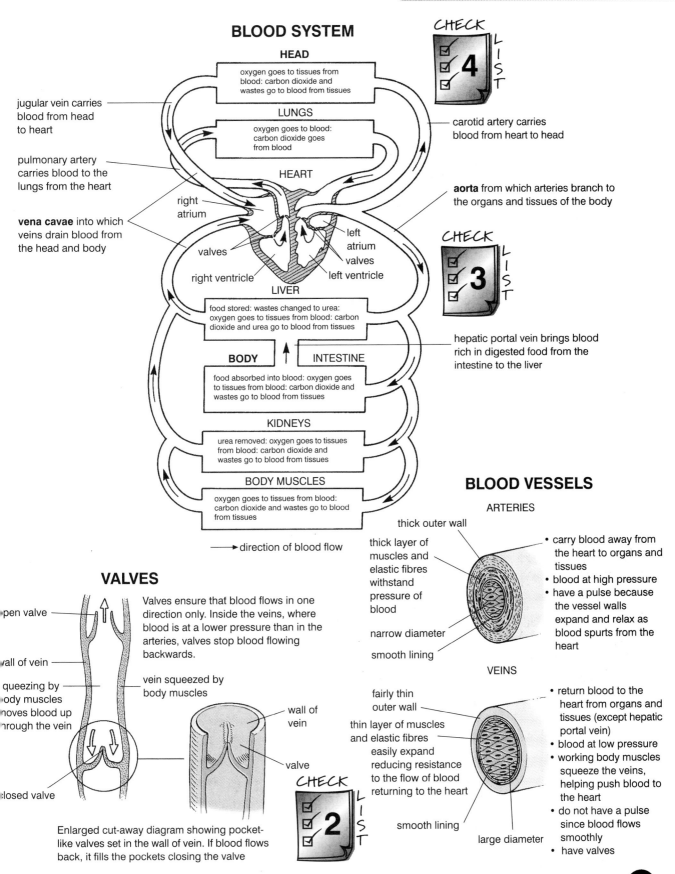

AIDS

AIDS (**A**cquired **I**mmune **D**eficiency **S**yndrome) is caused by the **H**uman **I**mmunodeficiency **V**irus (**HIV**). The virus attacks a particular type of lymphocyte (see page 99).

As a result, a person infected with HIV has reduced protection from disease-causing microorganisms.

Once HIV has destroyed a number of lymphocytes, the diseases of AIDS develop. Common diseases include:

- pneumonia – a disease of the lungs
- thrush – a fungal infection
- Kaposi's sarcoma – a skin cancer.

Understanding heart disease

The **coronary arteries** supply blood to the heart muscle, as shown in the diagram. The lining of blood vessels can be damaged and roughened by a fatty deposit called **atheroma**. The build-up of atheroma in the coronary arteries is one cause of **heart disease**. It increases the risk of blood clots forming. A blood clot in the coronary arteries can interrupt the blood supply to the heart, and the person suffers a **heart attack**.

The symptoms are

- severe pain in the chest, neck and arms
- sweating
- faintness and sickness.

The clot is called a **thrombus**, and the blockage a **thrombosis**.

The diagram shows some of the factors affecting the risk of a person developing heart disease.

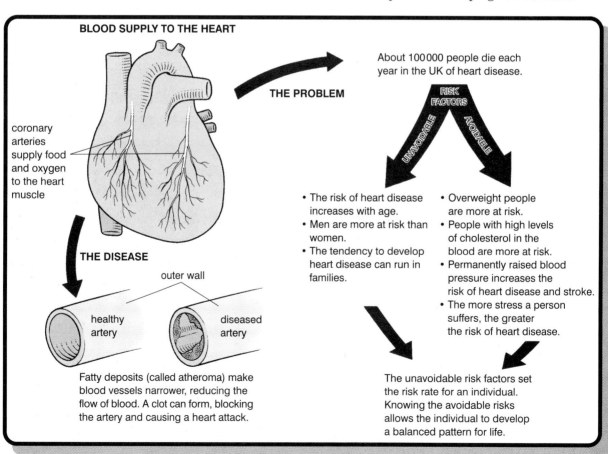

BLOOD SUPPLY TO THE HEART

coronary arteries supply food and oxygen to the heart muscle

THE PROBLEM

About 100 000 people die each year in the UK of heart disease.

RISK FACTORS

UNAVOIDABLE **AVOIDABLE**

- The risk of heart disease increases with age.
- Men are more at risk than women.
- The tendency to develop heart disease can run in families.

- Overweight people are more at risk.
- People with high levels of cholesterol in the blood are more at risk.
- Permanently raised blood pressure increases the risk of heart disease and stroke.
- The more stress a person suffers, the greater the risk of heart disease.

THE DISEASE

outer wall

healthy artery   diseased artery

Fatty deposits (called atheroma) make blood vessels narrower, reducing the flow of blood. A clot can form, blocking the artery and causing a heart attack.

The unavoidable risk factors set the risk rate for an individual. Knowing the avoidable risks allows the individual to develop a balanced pattern for life.

The risk of heart disease

5.6 Senses and the nervous system

preview

At the end of this section you will know that:
- **stimuli are converted by receptors into signals called nerve impulses, to which the body can respond**
- **neurones (nerve cells) conduct nerve impulses to muscles, which respond by contracting**
- **muscles are called effectors**
- **nerves are formed from bundles of neurones and are the link between stimulus and response.**

The process runs:

stimulus → receptor → nerves → effector → response

Stimulus and response

A **stimulus** is a change in the environment which causes a living organism to take action. A **response** is the action that the living organism takes. The **nervous system** links stimuli and responses. This is the sequence of events:

★ **Sensory receptor cells** detect stimuli and convert them into **nerve impulses**, to which the body can respond.

★ Nerve impulses are minute electrical disturbances.

★ **Neurones** (nerve cells) conduct nerve impulses to **effectors** (muscles or glands). Muscles respond to nerve impulses by contracting; glands respond by secreting substances. For example, the adrenal glands respond to nerve impulses by producing the hormone adrenaline, which helps the body cope with sudden stress.

> HORMONES
> Pages 83, 86–7.

The nervous system

On pages 80–1 is the concept map for **the nervous system**. The numbers on the concept map refer to the checklist.

Checklist for the nervous system

1 ★ Each **nerve** of the nervous system consists of a bundle of **neurones**.

  ★ Each neurone transmits nerve impulses to an **effector** (muscle or gland).

  ★ Nerve impulses are minute electrical disturbances which carry information about stimuli.

  ★ Nerve impulses stimulate effectors to respond to stimuli in a useful way.

  ★ A nerve impulse takes just milliseconds to travel along a neurone.

2 ★ **Neurotransmitter** is a chemical substance released from the end of a neurone into the **synapse**.

  ★ Neurotransmitter is produced only from the end of the neurone before the synapse.

  As a result, nerve impulses always travel *from* the receptor *to* the effector.

3 ★ **Reflex responses** happen before the brain has had time to process the nerve impulses carrying the information about the stimulus.

  ★ When the brain catches up with events, it brings about the next set of reactions – such as a shout of pain.

  ★ **Ascending fibres** form synapses with sensory neurones. The ascending fibres carry nerve impulses to the brain.

  As a result, the brain receives information about the stimulus causing the reflex response.

  ★ Nerve impulses from the brain are transmitted to effectors by the **descending fibres**, which synapse with motor neurones.

  As a result, the reflex response is brought under conscious control.

4 ★ The human brain weighs approximately 1.3 kg and occupies a volume of about 1500 cm^3.

  ★ Around 6 million neurones make up 1 cm^3 of brain matter.

  ★ Memory and learning are under the brain's control.

  ★ Different drugs affect the brain. For example, ethanol (the alcohol in beers, wines and spirits) depresses the activity of the cerebral cortex, affecting judgement and the control of movement.

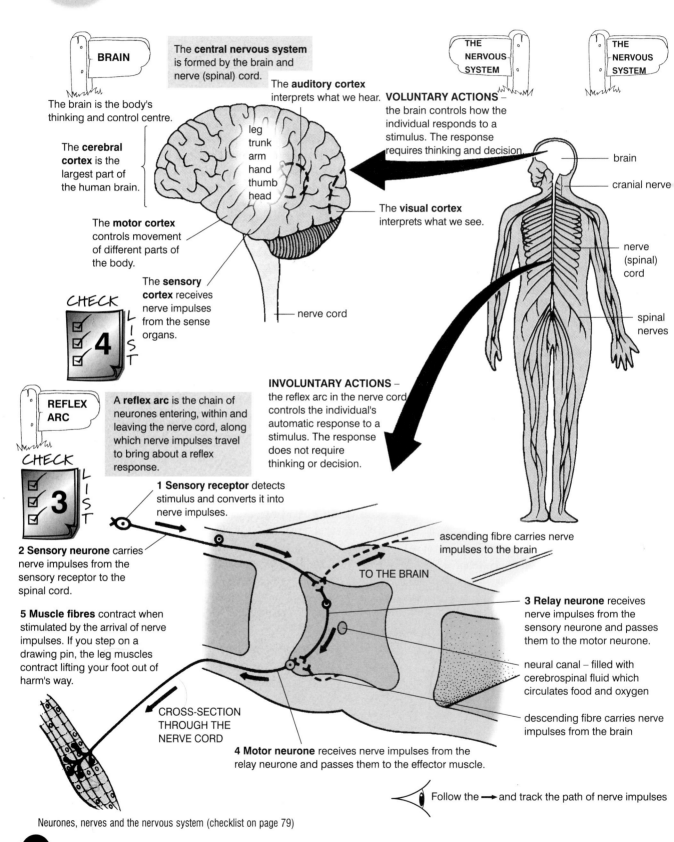

BRAIN

The **central nervous system** is formed by the brain and nerve (spinal) cord.

The brain is the body's thinking and control centre.

The **cerebral cortex** is the largest part of the human brain.

The **auditory cortex** interprets what we hear.

leg
trunk
arm
hand
thumb
head

The **motor cortex** controls movement of different parts of the body.

The **visual cortex** interprets what we see.

The **sensory cortex** receives nerve impulses from the sense organs.

CHECK **4** LIST

— nerve cord

THE NERVOUS SYSTEM

THE NERVOUS SYSTEM

VOLUNTARY ACTIONS – the brain controls how the individual responds to a stimulus. The response requires thinking and decision.

— brain

— cranial nerve

— nerve (spinal) cord

— spinal nerves

REFLEX ARC

A **reflex arc** is the chain of neurones entering, within and leaving the nerve cord, along which nerve impulses travel to bring about a reflex response.

CHECK **3** LIST

INVOLUNTARY ACTIONS – the reflex arc in the nerve cord controls the individual's automatic response to a stimulus. The response does not require thinking or decision.

1 Sensory receptor detects stimulus and converts it into nerve impulses.

2 Sensory neurone carries nerve impulses from the sensory receptor to the spinal cord.

ascending fibre carries nerve impulses to the brain

TO THE BRAIN

5 Muscle fibres contract when stimulated by the arrival of nerve impulses. If you step on a drawing pin, the leg muscles contract lifting your foot out of harm's way.

3 Relay neurone receives nerve impulses from the sensory neurone and passes them to the motor neurone.

neural canal – filled with cerebrospinal fluid which circulates food and oxygen

descending fibre carries nerve impulses from the brain

CROSS-SECTION THROUGH THE NERVE CORD

4 Motor neurone receives nerve impulses from the relay neurone and passes them to the effector muscle.

Follow the ➤ and track the path of nerve impulses

Neurones, nerves and the nervous system (checklist on page 79)

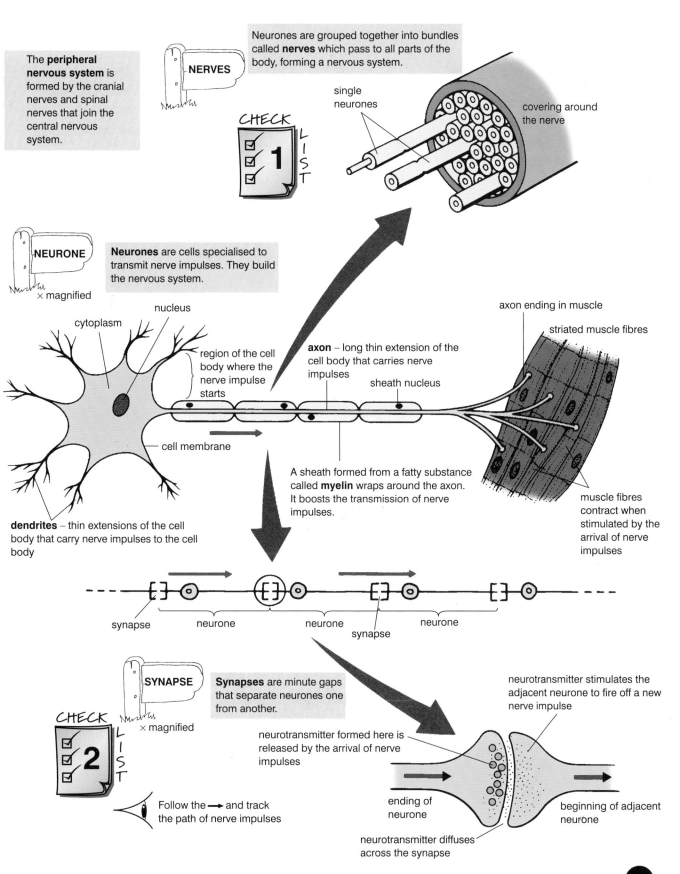

The **peripheral nervous system** is formed by the cranial nerves and spinal nerves that join the central nervous system.

Neurones are grouped together into bundles called **nerves** which pass to all parts of the body, forming a nervous system.

NERVES

CHECK LIST 1

single neurones

covering around the nerve

NEURONE
× magnified

Neurones are cells specialised to transmit nerve impulses. They build the nervous system.

cytoplasm

nucleus

region of the cell body where the nerve impulse starts

cell membrane

dendrites – thin extensions of the cell body that carry nerve impulses to the cell body

axon – long thin extension of the cell body that carries nerve impulses

sheath nucleus

A sheath formed from a fatty substance called **myelin** wraps around the axon. It boosts the transmission of nerve impulses.

axon ending in muscle

striated muscle fibres

muscle fibres contract when stimulated by the arrival of nerve impulses

synapse   neurone   neurone   neurone

synapse

SYNAPSE
× magnified

Synapses are minute gaps that separate neurones one from another.

CHECK LIST 2

Follow the ➡ and track the path of nerve impulses

neurotransmitter formed here is released by the arrival of nerve impulses

neurotransmitter stimulates the adjacent neurone to fire off a new nerve impulse

ending of neurone

beginning of adjacent neurone

neurotransmitter diffuses across the synapse

5.7 Sense organs

At the end of this section you will know that:

- the sense organs consist of sensory cells which are adapted to detect a particular type of stimulus.

Handy hint

The sensory cells of the

- **S**kin detect heat and cold, touch and pain
- **N**ose detect chemicals
- **E**ye detect light
- **E**ar detect sound
- **T**ongue detect chemicals.

Thinking of the mnemonic **SNEET** will help you remember the major sense organs of the body.

Sensing the surroundings

On pages 84–5 is the concept map for **sense organs**. The numbers refer to the checklist below.

Checklist for sense organs

1 ★ **Tears** lubricate the surface of the eye. They contain the enzyme **lysozyme** which kills bacteria.

★ The **iris** of the eye is usually coloured brown, blue or green.

★ A pair of human eyes contains around 130 million **rods** and 7 million **cones**.

★ **Cone** cells are packed most densely in the region of the **fovea** and respond to bright light.

As a result, objects are seen most clearly if looked at straight on.

★ **Rod** cells occur mostly near the edges of the retina and respond to dim light.

As a result, objects are seen less clearly out of the corner of the eye.

2 ★ Loudness is measured in **decibels**. The faintest sound that the ear can hear is defined as zero decibels.

★ The response of the ear to different levels of loudness varies with frequency. The ear is most sensitive to frequencies around 3000 Hz, and can detect the softest sounds. It is completely insensitive to sounds over 18 000 Hz and cannot detect them.

★ The walls of the ear tube produce wax, which keeps the eardrum soft and supple.

3 ★ The nerve impulses from **temperature receptors** are interpreted by the brain, enabling us to feel whether our surroundings are hot or cold.

★ Sensitivity to **touch** depends on which part of the body is stimulated. The tip of the tongue and the fingertips can distinguish between two pin pricks 1.0 mm apart. Two pinpricks on the thigh may have to be more than 60 mm apart before they are detected as separate stimuli.

4 ★ **Taste buds** help us to decide whether food is safe. A bitter taste is usually a warning signal not to swallow.

★ **Smell** is defined as the detection of substances carried in the air.

★ To be detected, substances which are tasted or smelt must first be dissolved in the watery environment covering the receptor cells.

Check the vibrations

In the concept map, notice the different structures in the ear vibrating in response to sound waves striking the eardrum. The sequence reads:

- eardrum
- bones of the middle ear
- oval window
- fluid in the cochlea
- basilar membrane
- stimulated hair cells (receptors) fire off nerve impulses to the brain along the auditory nerve

Fact file

★ The ear becomes less and less sensitive if it is regularly exposed to very loud sounds. At noisy discos, you can protect your ears by plugging them with cotton wool.

★ In most humans the ear lobe (pinna) is fixed. Cats and dogs, however, can adjust the pinna and turn it towards sources of sound.

★ A cat's tongue contains very few taste receptors which respond to sugar. Cats, therefore, are among the few animals that do not prefer substances with a sweet taste.

The eye at work

Look up from this page and gaze out of the window at some distant object. Your eye lens becomes thinner to keep your vision in focus. This change in lens shape to keep a nearby object and then a distant object in focus is called **accommodation**.

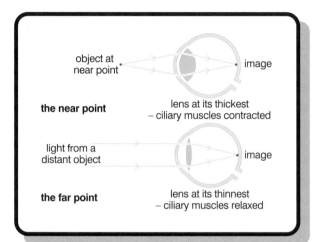

object at near point

image

the near point

lens at its thickest – ciliary muscles contracted

light from a distant object

image

the far point

lens at its thinnest – ciliary muscles relaxed

Accommodation keeps objects in focus

Fact file

★ Human eyes are damaged by ultraviolet light. However, insects' eyes can see in ultraviolet light.

★ A normal eye can see clearly any object from far away (at the **far point**) to 25 cm from the eye (the **near point**).

★ The image of an object on the retina is inverted, but the brain interprets it so you see it the right way up.

Light control

The **iris** controls the amount of light entering the eye. Bright light causes a **reflex response**:

★ The muscle of the iris contracts.

As a result, the pupil narrows.

As a result, the amount of light entering the eye is reduced.

In dim light:

★ the muscle of the iris relaxes.

As a result, the pupil widens.

As a result, the amount of light entering the eye is increased.

5.8 Hormones

preview

At the end of this section you will know that:

● chemicals called hormones regulate the activities of the body

● hormones are produced in the tissues of endocrine glands

● endocrine glands are ductless glands – they release their hormones directly into the bloodstream

● hormones circulate in the blood and cause specific effects on the body

● the tissue on which a particular hormone or group of hormones acts is called a target tissue.

The hormonal system

The blood system is the link between a hormone and its **target tissue**. The sequence reads:

$$\text{endocrine gland} \xrightarrow{\text{produces}} \text{hormone} \xrightarrow{\text{circulates}} \text{blood} \xrightarrow{\text{affects}} \text{target tissue}$$

Hormones affect many of the body's activities. For example, the hormones **insulin** and **glucagon** help regulate the level of glucose in the blood and cope with the surge of glucose at mealtimes and when you eat a snack, such as a bar of chocolate.

Fact file

Most hormones produce their effects rather slowly. They bring about long-term changes in the body such as growth and sexual development.

How hormones work

On pages 86–7 is the concept map which revises **hormones**. The numbers on the concept map refer to the checklist on page 88.

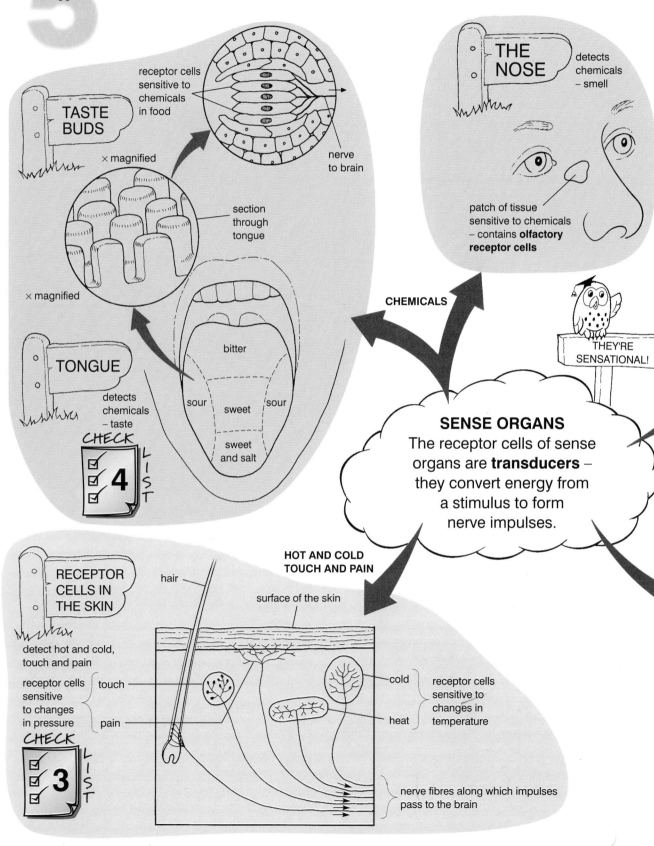

TASTE BUDS

receptor cells sensitive to chemicals in food

× magnified

section through tongue

× magnified

nerve to brain

TONGUE

detects chemicals – taste

bitter

sour

sweet

sour

sweet and salt

CHECK **4** LIST

THE NOSE

detects chemicals – smell

patch of tissue sensitive to chemicals – contains **olfactory receptor cells**

CHEMICALS

THEY'RE SENSATIONAL!

SENSE ORGANS
The receptor cells of sense organs are **transducers** – they convert energy from a stimulus to form nerve impulses.

HOT AND COLD TOUCH AND PAIN

RECEPTOR CELLS IN THE SKIN

detect hot and cold, touch and pain

receptor cells sensitive to changes in pressure

hair

surface of the skin

touch

pain

cold

heat

receptor cells sensitive to changes in temperature

nerve fibres along which impulses pass to the brain

CHECK **3** LIST

Sense organs (checklist on page 82)

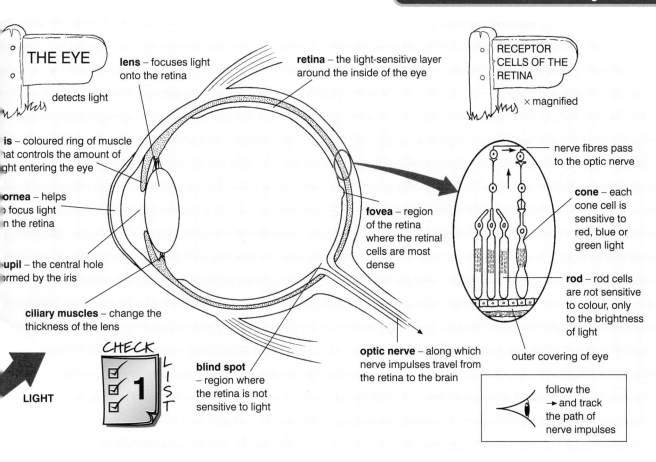

THE EYE

detects light

lens – focuses light onto the retina

retina – the light-sensitive layer around the inside of the eye

is – coloured ring of muscle that controls the amount of ght entering the eye

ornea – helps focus light n the retina

upil – the central hole ormed by the iris

ciliary muscles – change the thickness of the lens

blind spot – region where the retina is not sensitive to light

fovea – region of the retina where the retinal cells are most dense

optic nerve – along which nerve impulses travel from the retina to the brain

LIGHT

CHECK LIST 1

RECEPTOR CELLS OF THE RETINA

× magnified

nerve fibres pass to the optic nerve

cone – each cone cell is sensitive to red, blue or green light

rod – rod cells are *not* sensitive to colour, only to the brightness of light

outer covering of eye

follow the → and track the path of nerve impulses

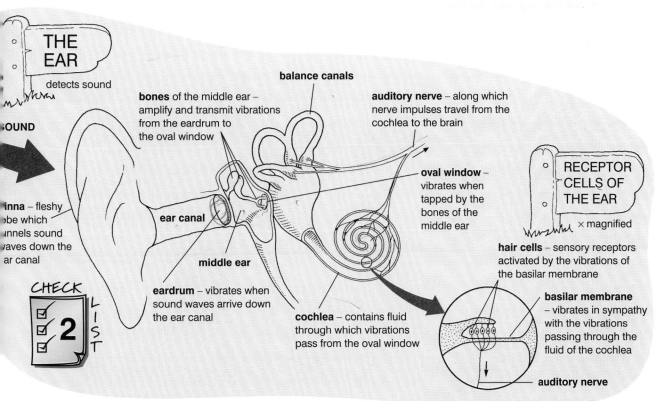

THE EAR

detects sound

SOUND

balance canals

bones of the middle ear – amplify and transmit vibrations from the eardrum to the oval window

auditory nerve – along which nerve impulses travel from the cochlea to the brain

inna – fleshy obe which unnels sound waves down the ar canal

ear canal

middle ear

eardrum – vibrates when sound waves arrive down the ear canal

cochlea – contains fluid through which vibrations pass from the oval window

oval window – vibrates when tapped by the bones of the middle ear

RECEPTOR CELLS OF THE EAR

× magnified

hair cells – sensory receptors activated by the vibrations of the basilar membrane

basilar membrane – vibrates in sympathy with the vibrations passing through the fluid of the cochlea

auditory nerve

CHECK LIST 2

85

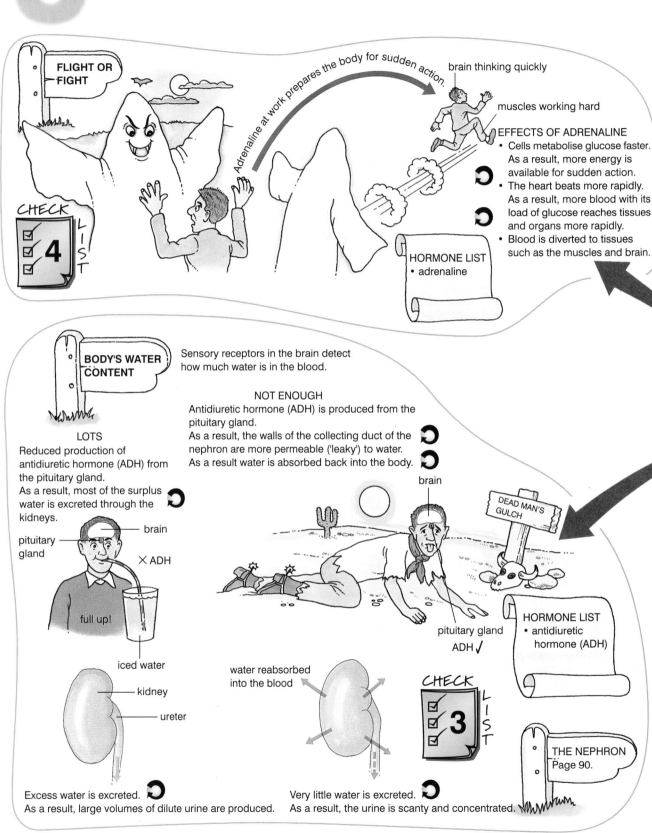

FLIGHT OR FIGHT

CHECK LIST **4**

Adrenaline at work prepares the body for sudden action.

brain thinking quickly

muscles working hard

HORMONE LIST
• adrenaline

EFFECTS OF ADRENALINE
• Cells metabolise glucose faster. As a result, more energy is available for sudden action.
• The heart beats more rapidly. As a result, more blood with its load of glucose reaches tissues and organs more rapidly.
• Blood is diverted to tissues such as the muscles and brain.

BODY'S WATER CONTENT

Sensory receptors in the brain detect how much water is in the blood.

NOT ENOUGH
Antidiuretic hormone (ADH) is produced from the pituitary gland.
As a result, the walls of the collecting duct of the nephron are more permeable ('leaky') to water.
As a result water is absorbed back into the body.

brain

DEAD MAN'S GULCH

LOTS
Reduced production of antidiuretic hormone (ADH) from the pituitary gland.
As a result, most of the surplus water is excreted through the kidneys.

brain

pituitary gland

✕ ADH

full up!

iced water

kidney

ureter

water reabsorbed into the blood

pituitary gland
ADH ✓

HORMONE LIST
• antidiuretic hormone (ADH)

CHECK LIST **3**

THE NEPHRON
Page 90.

Excess water is excreted.
As a result, large volumes of dilute urine are produced.

Very little water is excreted.
As a result, the urine is scanty and concentrated.

Hormones at work (checklist on page 88)

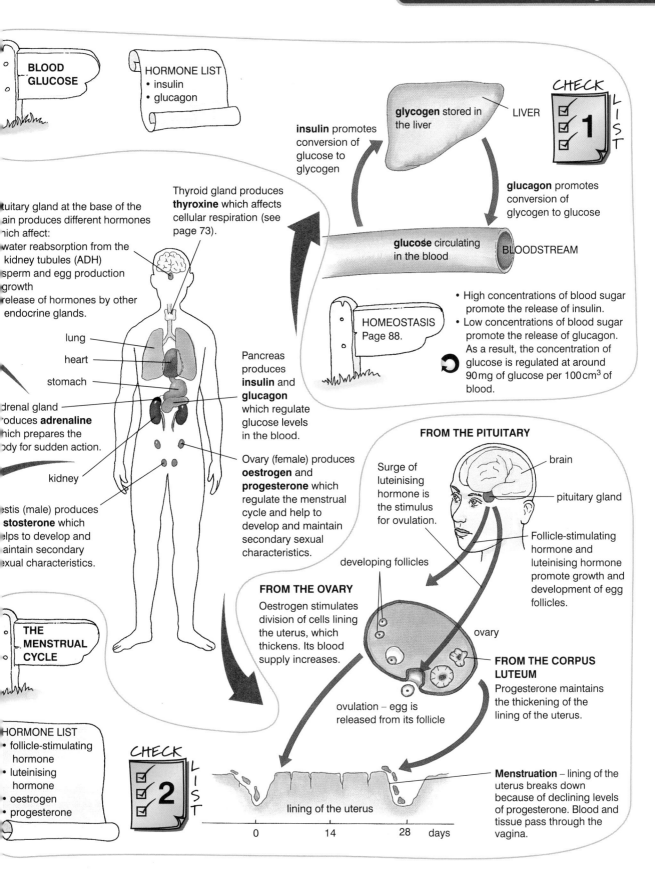

BLOOD GLUCOSE

HORMONE LIST
• insulin
• glucagon

glycogen stored in the liver

LIVER

CHECK **1** LIST

insulin promotes conversion of glucose to glycogen

glucagon promotes conversion of glycogen to glucose

glucose circulating in the blood

BLOODSTREAM

HOMEOSTASIS
Page 88.

• High concentrations of blood sugar promote the release of insulin.
• Low concentrations of blood sugar promote the release of glucagon. As a result, the concentration of glucose is regulated at around 90 mg of glucose per 100 cm³ of blood.

Thyroid gland produces **thyroxine** which affects cellular respiration (see page 73).

tuitary gland at the base of the ain produces different hormones hich affect:
 water reabsorption from the kidney tubules (ADH)
 sperm and egg production
 growth
 release of hormones by other endocrine glands.

lung

heart

stomach

drenal gland oduces **adrenaline** hich prepares the dy for sudden action.

kidney

Pancreas produces **insulin** and **glucagon** which regulate glucose levels in the blood.

stis (male) produces **stosterone** which lps to develop and aintain secondary exual characteristics.

Ovary (female) produces **oestrogen** and **progesterone** which regulate the menstrual cycle and help to develop and maintain secondary sexual characteristics.

FROM THE PITUITARY

Surge of luteinising hormone is the stimulus for ovulation.

brain

pituitary gland

Follicle-stimulating hormone and luteinising hormone promote growth and development of egg follicles.

developing follicles

FROM THE OVARY
Oestrogen stimulates division of cells lining the uterus, which thickens. Its blood supply increases.

ovary

FROM THE CORPUS LUTEUM
Progesterone maintains the thickening of the lining of the uterus.

THE MENSTRUAL CYCLE

ovulation – egg is released from its follicle

HORMONE LIST
• follicle-stimulating hormone
• luteinising hormone
• oestrogen
• progesterone

CHECK **2** LIST

lining of the uterus

0   14   28   days

Menstruation – lining of the uterus breaks down because of declining levels of progesterone. Blood and tissue pass through the vagina.

Checklist for hormones at work

1 ★ If the pancreas does not produce enough insulin, a condition called **diabetes mellitus** occurs.

As a result, the glucose level in the blood becomes dangerously high and can cause kidney failure and blindness.

★ People suffering from diabetes (**diabetics**) are taught to inject themselves regularly with insulin to lower their blood glucose level.

★ Glycogen is a polysaccharide whose molecules consist of hundreds of glucose units.

2 ★ The human female usually produces one mature egg each month from the onset of **puberty** (age 11–14 years) to the approach of the **menopause** (age about 45 years). Egg production becomes more irregular and then stops at the menopause (average age around 51 years).

★ The contraceptive pill contains one or both of the hormones oestrogen and progesterone. The hormones stop the ovaries from producing eggs.

3 ★ **Diuresis** is the flow of urine from the body. Antidiuretic hormone counteracts diuresis.

As a result, the flow of urine from the body is reduced.

★ Ethanol (the alcohol in beer, wine and spirits) increases diuresis.

4 ★ Unlike most hormones, adrenaline produces its effect very quickly.

As a result, the body is able to respond to sudden shock or danger.

Fact file – guys and gals

Secondary sexual characteristics are the physical features which distinguish boys from girls. Testosterone helps develop and maintain the secondary sexual characteristics of boys. Oestrogen and progesterone help develop and maintain the secondary sexual characteristics of girls.

guys	gals
pubic hair develops	pubic hair develops
penis gets larger	breasts develop and fat is laid down in the thighs
voice breaks	menstruation starts
hair grows on armpits, chest, face and legs	hair grows on armpits

Secondary sexual characteristics

5.9 Maintaining the internal environment

preview

At the end of this section you will:

● **understand that for cells to work efficiently, the composition of the tissue fluid which surrounds them should be kept fairly constant**

● **know about the important systems which maintain a constant environment in the body: the pancreas and liver (blood glucose), the kidneys (water content) and the skin (temperature).**

Conditions in the body

The cells of the body work efficiently when they are

- at an appropriate temperature
- supplied with an appropriate mixture and concentration of substances
- supplied with sufficient water
- at an appropriate acidity/alkalinity (pH).

These conditions are part of the body's **internal environment**. Different mechanisms help regulate the body, keeping its internal environment fairly constant. Keeping conditions constant is called **homeostasis**.

★ The **skin** regulates the body's temperature.

★ The **kidneys** regulate the concentration of salts in the blood, and the water content of the body.

LIVER AND PANCREAS Page 65.

★ The **liver** and **pancreas** regulate the concentration of sugar in the blood.

Homeostasis

Homeostasis depends on **negative feedback** mechanisms, which enable different processes to correct themselves when they change. In other words, the processes of life are **self-adjusting**. A level of a chemical or a temperature that deviates from a **set point** (a normal value) is returned to that set point. The menstrual cycle pictured on page 87 illustrates the principles. Rising levels of follicle-stimulating hormone and luteinising hormone stimulate the ovaries to produce the hormone oestrogen. Increasing levels of oestrogen feed back negatively, inhibiting further release of follicle-stimulating hormone. The level of the hormone returns to normal, its role of promoting the growth of egg follicles complete.

On pages 90–1 is the concept map for **homeostasis**. The numbers on the concept map refer to the checklist of points below. Study the concept map and its checklist carefully.

Checklist for homeostasis

1 ★ Each kidney consists of about one million tiny tubules called **nephrons**.

   ★ The nephron is the working unit of the kidney. It is the structure that brings about homeostatic control of the:
- concentration of salts in the blood
- water content of the body.

   The kidney tubules are also responsible for the excretion of urea and other wastes from the body.

2 ★ Hair is made of the protein keratin.

   ★ **Goose pimples** are bumps on the skin formed when empty hair follicles contract in response to cold.

Fact file

★ Liver metabolism releases a lot of heat energy, which is distributed all over the body by blood. Humans (and other mammals and birds) have a high metabolic rate, which releases a large amount of heat. This is why mammals and birds are **warm blooded**.

Copy and complete this Mind Map to help your revision of co-ordination in humans and plants.

5.10 Support and movement preview

At the end of this section you will:
- **be able to identify different types of skeleton**
- **understand the principal components of the human skeleton**
- **know the action of antagonistic muscles**
- **understand the pentadactyl arrangement of bones in the limbs of birds and mammals**
- **be able to analyse locomotion through water and air.**

Making the link

The skeleton supports the body, and provides surfaces for the attachment of muscles. Nerve impulses stimulate muscles to contract. They pull on the skeleton, moving it. The sequence reads:

$$\text{nerve impulses} \xrightarrow{\text{stimulate}} \text{muscles contract} \xrightarrow{\text{pull}} \text{skeleton} \rightarrow \text{MOVES}$$

Skeletons

There are three types of skeleton, listed below.

1 **Endoskeletons** are found in vertebrates. The skeleton lies inside the body, surrounded by the soft tissue. It is made of **bone** and **cartilage**.

2 **Exoskeletons** are found in insects and other arthropods. The skeleton is made of hard plates (see page 12) which surround the body. The plates consist of the polysaccharide **chitin**, protein and other substances.

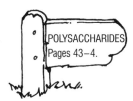

POLYSACCHARIDES
Pages 43–4.

3 **Hydrostatic skeletons** are found in the larger worms. The skeleton consists of a body space filled with fluid under pressure.

The human skeleton is shown on page 92.

CONTROLLING WATER CONTENT

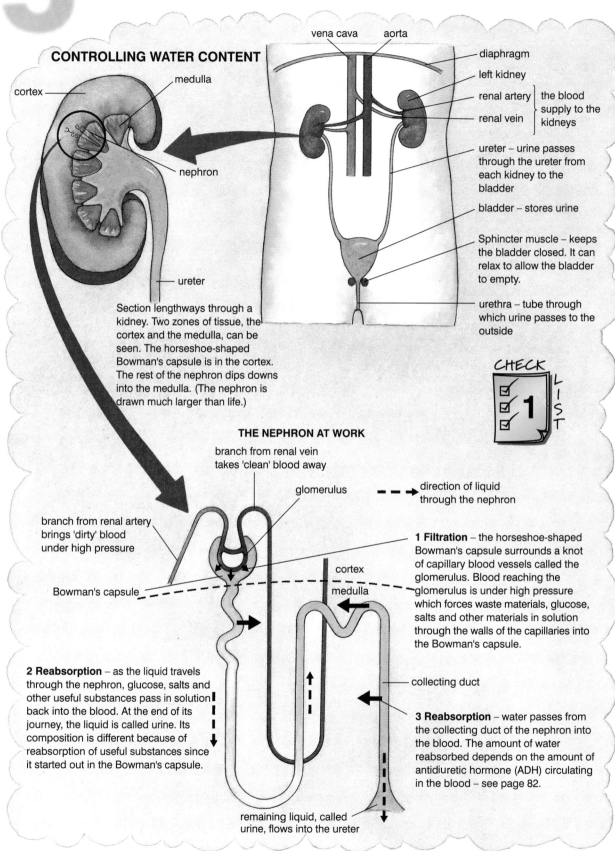

cortex

medulla

nephron

ureter

vena cava   aorta

diaphragm

left kidney

renal artery ⎫ the blood
renal vein ⎬ supply to the
            ⎭ kidneys

ureter – urine passes through the ureter from each kidney to the bladder

bladder – stores urine

Sphincter muscle – keeps the bladder closed. It can relax to allow the bladder to empty.

urethra – tube through which urine passes to the outside

Section lengthways through a kidney. Two zones of tissue, the cortex and the medulla, can be seen. The horseshoe-shaped Bowman's capsule is in the cortex. The rest of the nephron dips downs into the medulla. (The nephron is drawn much larger than life.)

CHECK ☑☑☑ 1 LIST

THE NEPHRON AT WORK

branch from renal vein takes 'clean' blood away

glomerulus

- - - → direction of liquid through the nephron

branch from renal artery brings 'dirty' blood under high pressure

cortex
medulla

Bowman's capsule

1 Filtration – the horseshoe-shaped Bowman's capsule surrounds a knot of capillary blood vessels called the glomerulus. Blood reaching the glomerulus is under high pressure which forces waste materials, glucose, salts and other materials in solution through the walls of the capillaries into the Bowman's capsule.

collecting duct

2 Reabsorption – as the liquid travels through the nephron, glucose, salts and other useful substances pass in solution back into the blood. At the end of its journey, the liquid is called urine. Its composition is different because of reabsorption of useful substances since it started out in the Bowman's capsule.

3 Reabsorption – water passes from the collecting duct of the nephron into the blood. The amount of water reabsorbed depends on the amount of antidiuretic hormone (ADH) circulating in the blood – see page 82.

remaining liquid, called urine, flows into the ureter

MAINTAINING A CONSTANT INTERNAL ENVIRONMENT

CONTROLLING TEMPERATURE

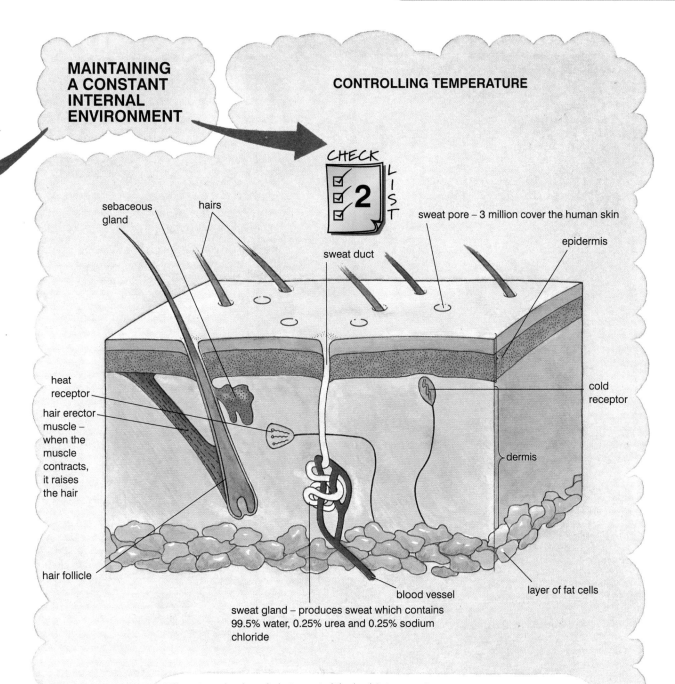

CHECK LIST **2**

sebaceous gland

hairs

sweat duct

sweat pore – 3 million cover the human skin

epidermis

heat receptor

hair erector muscle – when the muscle contracts, it raises the hair

cold receptor

dermis

hair follicle

blood vessel

layer of fat cells

sweat gland – produces sweat which contains 99.5% water, 0.25% urea and 0.25% sodium chloride

Different mechanisms help to control the body's temperature:
- Hairs raised by erector muscles trap a layer of air which insulates the body in cold weather (air is a poor conductor of heat). In warm weather, the hair is lowered and no air is trapped.
- Fat insulates the body and reduces heat loss.
- Sweat cools the body because it carries heat energy away from the body as it evaporates.
- Millions of temperature-sensitive sense receptors cover the skin. Nerves connect them to the brain which controls the body's response to changes in temperature in the environment.
- When it is warm, blood vessels in the skin dilate (**vasodilation**). More blood flows through the vessels in the skin and loses heat to the environment. In cold weather, the blood vessels in the skin constrict (**vasoconstriction**) and less heat is lost to the environment.

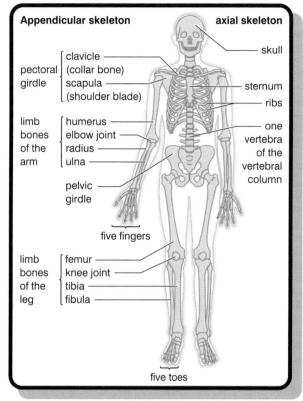

Appendicular skeleton — axial skeleton

pectoral girdle	clavicle (collar bone), scapula (shoulder blade)
limb bones of the arm	humerus, elbow joint, radius, ulna
	pelvic girdle
	five fingers
limb bones of the leg	femur, knee joint, tibia, fibula
	five toes

skull — sternum — ribs — one vertebra of the vertebral column

The human skeleton

★ **Joints** are formed where the bones of the skeleton connect to one another.

★ **Ligaments** hold joints together.

★ **Tendons** attach muscles to the skeleton.

As muscles contract and relax, they move the bones at the joints.

There are two parts to the human skeleton.

1 The **axial skeleton** consists of the
   • **skull**, which encloses and protects the brain.
   • **vertebral column** (backbone), made up of a series of bones called **vertebrae**. At the centre of each vertebra is a channel called the **neural canal**, which forms a continuous space in the vertebral column through which runs the **nerve cord**. The vertebral column supports the skull and the **pectoral** and **pelvic** girdles.

BRAIN AND NERVE CORD Pages 79–81.

• **ribs**, which form a bony cage protecting the heart and lungs.

The axial skeleton protects the delicate tissues and organs of the body.

2 The **appendicular skeleton** consists of the
   • **pelvic girdle**, which links the legs with the vertebral column. Its rigid framework allows forces on the legs to be transmitted to the rest of the body.
   • **pectoral girdle**, which links the arms with the vertebral column. Its flexibility gives the shoulders and arms freedom of movement.
   • **limb bones**, which in humans are long bones jointed at the elbows in the arms and at the knees in the legs. The limb bones also form joints with the girdles at the hips and shoulders, and with the hands at the wrists and the feet at the ankles. The joints at the elbows, knees, wrists and ankles enable the limbs to move freely.

Notice that the bones in each hand and foot are arranged as five **digits** (fingers and toes). The arrangement of digits and the long bones to which they are attached forms the **pentadactyl limb** ('penta' means five). The limbs of vertebrates (except most types of fish) are based on the pentadactyl arrangement – EVEN MY WINGS!

wing

Types of joint

The diagram below shows a section through the joint of the elbow. Notice how friction in the joint is reduced to a minimum. There are different types of joint.

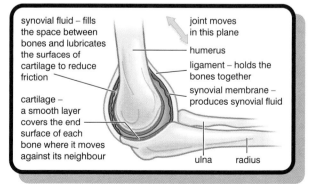

synovial fluid – fills the space between bones and lubricates the surfaces of cartilage to reduce friction

cartilage – a smooth layer covers the end surface of each bone where it moves against its neighbour

joint moves in this plane

humerus

ligament – holds the bones together

synovial membrane – produces synovial fluid

ulna   radius

The structure of the elbow joint

1 **Sutures** are fixed joints, for example the bones of the skull.

2 **Ball-and-socket joints** are formed where the upper long bones meet their respective girdles. The flexibility of these joints allows movement in all planes.

3 **Hinge joints** are formed at the elbow and knee. They allow movement in one plane only.

Bone and cartilage

Bone is a mixture of materials. **Collagen** is a flexible fibrous material made of protein, in which are deposited **calcium salts** that strengthen the bone.

Blood vessels run through canals in the bone called **Haversian canals**, supplying the bone tissue with oxygen and food substances.

Cartilage is softer than bone. It contains fewer calcium salts. In humans, cartilage covers the ends of limb bones and helps reduce friction in the joints as bones move over one another.

Muscles in action

Contracting muscles pull on bones. A muscle will pull a bone in one direction; another muscle will pull the same bone in the opposite direction. In other words, muscles work in pairs, where one muscle of the pair has the opposite effect to its partner. We call these pairs **antagonistic pairs**.

The diagram at the top of the next column shows you how the **biceps** and **triceps** raise (flex) and lower (extend) the arm.

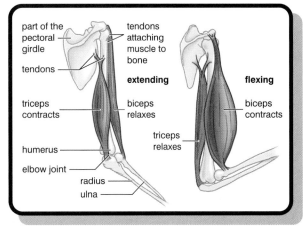

Moving the lower arm. The biceps and triceps work as an antagonistic pair of muscles.

How fish swim

The diagram overleaf shows how fish swim. Blocks of muscle attached to each side of the fish's vertebral column work as antagonistic pairs, flexing the body from side to side. The side of the body pushes against the water, driving the fish forward. The fins control the direction of movement, and stability.

- **Rolling** (rotation about the long axis of the body) and **yawing** (side-to-side movement of the head) are prevented by the dorsal and ventral fins.
- **Pitching** (the tendency to nose-dive) is prevented by the pectoral and pelvic fins.

How birds fly

Birds are adapted to fly in the following ways.

★ Hollow bones reduce weight.

★ Flight muscles move the wings up and down.

★ Feathers smoothly shape the body.

The diagram on pages 96–7 shows how birds fly.

Antagonistic pairs of muscles flap my wings!

This is my spot folks – fame at last!

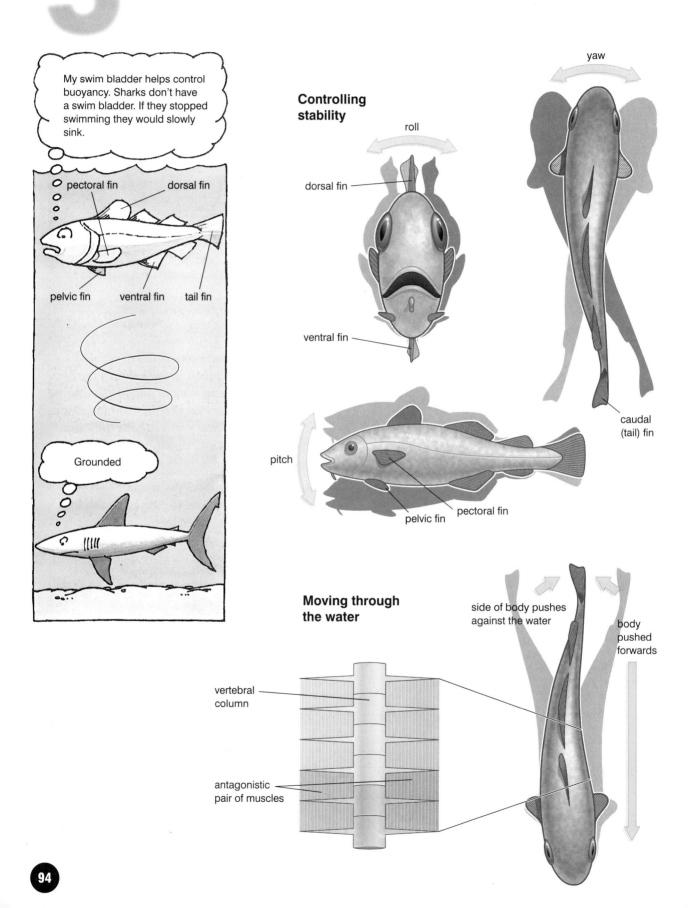

My swim bladder helps control buoyancy. Sharks don't have a swim bladder. If they stopped swimming they would slowly sink.

pectoral fin   dorsal fin

pelvic fin   ventral fin   tail fin

Grounded

Controlling stability

yaw

roll

dorsal fin

ventral fin

pitch

pelvic fin   pectoral fin

caudal (tail) fin

Moving through the water

side of body pushes against the water

body pushed forwards

vertebral column

antagonistic pair of muscles

round-up

How much have you improved?
Work out your improvement index on page 137.

1 Simple tests identify the nutrients in different foods. Match the nutrient in column **A** with the test result that identifies the nutrient in column **B**.

A nutrients	B test results
starch	forms a milky emulsion when mixed with warm dilute ethanol
glucose	produces a violet/purple colour when mixed with dilute sodium hydroxide and a few drops of copper sulphate solution
fat	produces a blue/black colour when mixed with a few drops of iodine solution
protein	produces an orange colour when heated with Benedict's solution

[4]

2 Match each enzyme in column **A** with its role in digestion in column **B**.

A enzymes	B roles
amylase	digests maltose to glucose
pepsin	digests fat to fatty acids and glycerol
lipase	digests starch to maltose
maltase	digests protein to polypeptides

[4]

3 Complete the following paragraph using the words below. Each word may be used once, more than once or not at all.

**thin   exhalation   fat   oxygen   inhalation   moist
carbon dioxide   exchange   alveoli   surface area**

The uptake of _____ and removal of _____ occur in the _____ of the lungs. These provide a large _____ for efficient gas _____. They are _____-walled, have an excellent blood supply, are _____ and kept well supplied with air by breathing. _____ takes air into the lungs; _____ removes air from the lungs. [9]

4 Distinguish between the following pairs of terms.
a) oxygenated and deoxygenated blood [4]
b) antibody and antigen [5]
c) HIV and AIDS [3]
d) haemoglobin and haemophilia [5]
e) thrombus and thrombosis [3]

5 The different parts of a motor nerve cell are listed in column **A**. Match each part with its description in column **B**.

A parts of a cell	B descriptions
axon	minute electrical disturbance
dendrite	boosts the transmission of nerve impulses
sheath	transmits nerve impulses from the cell body
nerve impulse	carries nerve impulses to the cell body

[4]

6 Explain the differences between the following pairs of terms.
a) blind spot and fovea
b) pupil and iris
c) cornea and retina [6]

7 How do endocrine glands differ from other glands in the body? [2]

8 Briefly explain how antidiuretic hormone (ADH) keeps the water content of the body steady. [2]

9 Briefly explain
a) why raised body hair helps us keep warm [3]
b) why sweating helps us keep cool. [2]

10 Relative to the size of the rest of the body, frog tadpoles have a long coiled digestive system and frog adults a short one. Briefly explain why this suggests that frog tadpoles are herbivores and frog adults are carnivores. [4]

11 Complete the following paragraph using the words below. Each word may be used once, more than once or not at all.

**dentist   hardest   softest   softens   keratin
acid   alkali   calcium   sugar**

Tooth enamel consists of _____ salts bound by the protein _____. This enamel is the _____ substance in the body. Bacteria in the mouth break down _____ to produce _____ which _____ the enamel, beginning the process of decay. Regular cleaning of the teeth and visits to the _____ help prevent tooth decay. [7]

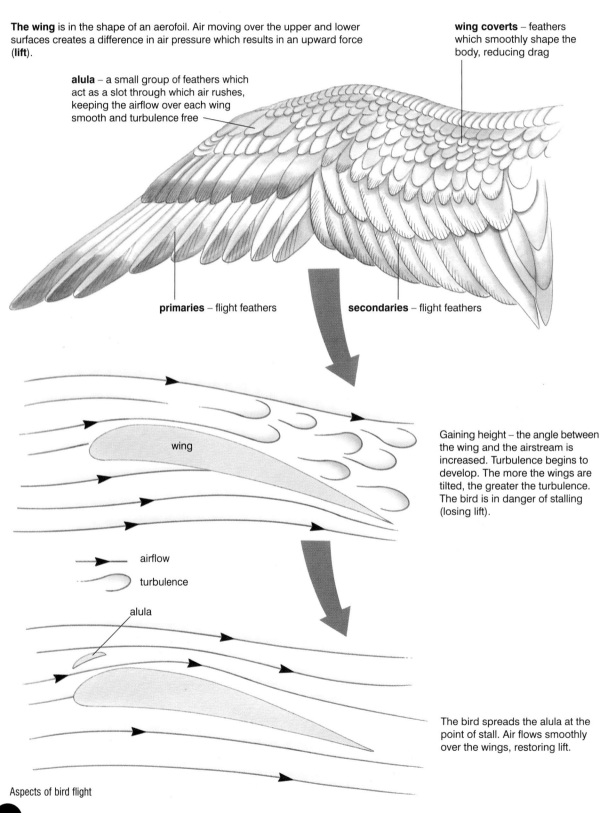

The wing is in the shape of an aerofoil. Air moving over the upper and lower surfaces creates a difference in air pressure which results in an upward force (**lift**).

alula – a small group of feathers which act as a slot through which air rushes, keeping the airflow over each wing smooth and turbulence free

wing coverts – feathers which smoothly shape the body, reducing drag

primaries – flight feathers

secondaries – flight feathers

wing

Gaining height – the angle between the wing and the airstream is increased. Turbulence begins to develop. The more the wings are tilted, the greater the turbulence. The bird is in danger of stalling (losing lift).

airflow

turbulence

alula

The bird spreads the alula at the point of stall. Air flows smoothly over the wings, restoring lift.

Aspects of bird flight

Upstroke – the recovery stroke which produces little air movement. The flight feathers separate and air passes through the gaps between them. Minimum air resistance means that the upstroke needs less effort.

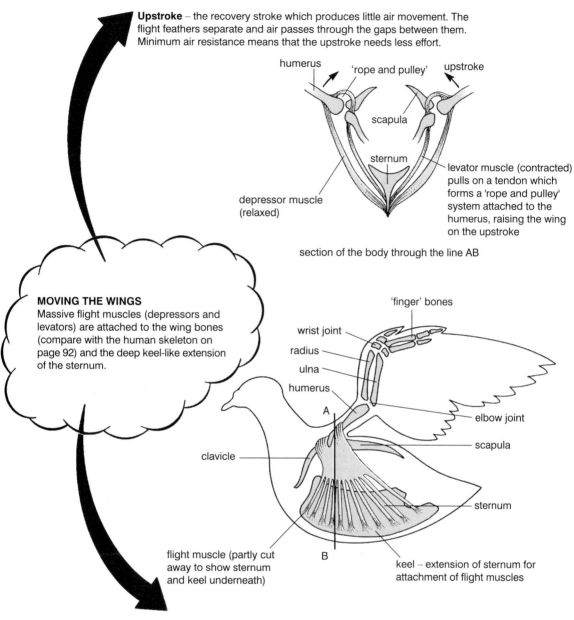

humerus

'rope and pulley'

upstroke

scapula

sternum

levator muscle (contracted) pulls on a tendon which forms a 'rope and pulley' system attached to the humerus, raising the wing on the upstroke

depressor muscle (relaxed)

section of the body through the line AB

MOVING THE WINGS
Massive flight muscles (depressors and levators) are attached to the wing bones (compare with the human skeleton on page 92) and the deep keel-like extension of the sternum.

'finger' bones

wrist joint

radius

ulna

humerus

A

elbow joint

scapula

sternum

clavicle

flight muscle (partly cut away to show sternum and keel underneath)

B

keel – extension of sternum for attachment of flight muscles

Downstroke – the power stroke pushes air downwards, supporting the weight of the bird. The flight feathers form an unbroken surface which provides maximum resistance to the air underneath, generating lift.

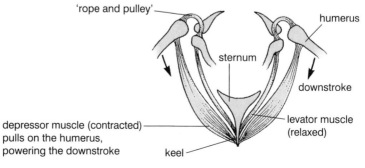

'rope and pulley'

humerus

sternum

downstroke

depressor muscle (contracted) pulls on the humerus, powering the downstroke

levator muscle (relaxed)

keel

section of the body through the line AB

Health and disease

How much do you already know?
Work out your score on pages 137–8.

Test yourself

1 Distinguish between non-infectious diseases and infectious diseases. Give *two* examples of each category. [7]

2 Match each body structure in column **A** with its role in the defence of the body against disease in column **B**.

A body structures	B roles
tear gland	produces sebum which kills bacteria and fungi
glands in the stomach wall	white cells produce antibodies which destroy antigens
skin	produce hydrochloric acid which kills bacteria
cilia lining the upper respiratory tract	produces the enzyme lysozyme which destroys bacteria
blood	sweep away mucus containing trapped micro-organisms and particles

[5]

3 Mumps and chickenpox are infectious diseases. Explain why we do not usually catch these diseases more than once in a lifetime. [5]

4 Distinguish between the following terms, which refer to aspects of tissue transplantation.
a) donor and recipient [2]
b) human lymphocyte antigens and red blood cell antigens [4]
c) immunosuppressive drugs and antibiotic drugs [4]

5 List five different methods used to preserve food. [5]

6 Describe how domestic rubbish may be disposed of. [3]

7 Distinguish between antiseptics, disinfectants and asepsis. [5]

8 Briefly explain how mosquitoes transmit the parasite that causes malaria from person to person. [7]

6.1 Introducing health and disease

preview

At the end of this section you will:
- **be able to distinguish between different categories of disease**
- **know about the defence mechanisms of the body**
- **understand the harmful effects of smoking**
- **understand the effects of drug abuse and solvent abuse on the body.**

What is disease?

There are several categories of disease.

Infectious diseases are caused by a range of organisms:

- **bacteria**, for example cholera, typhoid fever, tuberculosis, syphilis, gonorrhoea
- **viruses**, for example AIDS, 'flu, poliomyelitis, German measles
- **fungi**, for example thrush, athlete's foot, ringworm
- **protists**, for example malaria, sleeping sickness.

Non-infectious diseases develop because the body is not working properly:

- **cancer** – the uncontrolled division of cells leads to the development of a cancerous growth (**tumour**)
- **degenerative illnesses** – organs and tissues work less well with wear and tear, for example, joints become arthritic and sight and hearing deteriorate with age
- **allergies** – reactions to substances which are normally harmless, for example sensitivity to pollen and dust causes **hay fever**
- **deficiency** – a poor diet may deprive the body of vitamins and other essential substances, for example scurvy (deficiency of vitamin C), rickets (deficiency of vitamin D), kwashiorkor (deficiency of protein).

Genetic diseases result from genetic defects and may be inherited. There are around 4000 genetic diseases in humans. Genetic make-up also influences our vulnerability to other diseases such as diabetes and heart disease.

- **Down's syndrome** is caused by an extra copy of chromosome 21.
- **Sickle-cell anaemia** is caused by a mutation of the gene (**allele**) controlling the synthesis of the blood pigment haemoglobin.

MUTATION
Page 47.

- **Cystic fibrosis** is caused by the mutation of an allele on chromosome 7. The allele controls the production of a polypeptide important for the transport of chloride ions (Cl^-) across the cell membrane.

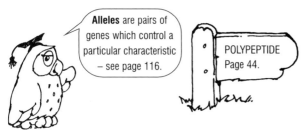

Alleles are pairs of genes which control a particular characteristic – see page 116.

POLYPEPTIDE
Page 44.

- **Haemophilia** is caused by the mutation of an allele on the X chromosome, as described below.

The allele on the X chromosome normally controls production of **factor VIII**, a substance required for the blood to clot. The defective allele is recessive. The Y chromosome does not carry a dominant allele to mask the effect of the defective recessive allele on the X chromosome. Therefore a man with the defective allele produces no factor VIII, and suffers from haemophilia. For a woman to suffer from haemophilia, she would have to receive the recessive allele from both her father and her mother – a rare occurrence. A woman who has the defective allele on *one* of the X chromosomes is called a **carrier**. She does not suffer from haemophilia because the normal allele on the other X chromosome is dominant.

Muscular dystrophy is another genetic disease linked to the X chromosome.

Fighting disease

The body's natural defences against disease are shown below. **Physical** barriers and **chemical** barriers keep us healthy for most of our lives.

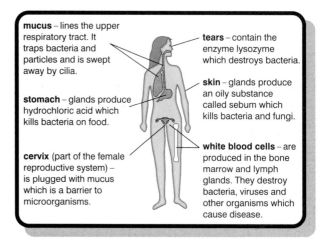

mucus – lines the upper respiratory tract. It traps bacteria and particles and is swept away by cilia.

stomach – glands produce hydrochloric acid which kills bacteria on food.

cervix (part of the female reproductive system) – is plugged with mucus which is a barrier to microorganisms.

tears – contain the enzyme lysozyme which destroys bacteria.

skin – glands produce an oily substance called sebum which kills bacteria and fungi.

white blood cells – are produced in the bone marrow and lymph glands. They destroy bacteria, viruses and other organisms which cause disease.

The body's natural defences against disease

White blood cells

Bacteria, viruses and other microorganisms may infect the blood and tissues of the body and cause disease. Two types of white blood cell, **lymphocytes** and **phagocytes**, protect the body. They work quickly to destroy bacteria, viruses or other cells or substances which the body does not recognise as its own. Such materials 'foreign' to the body are called **antigens**.

There are two types of lymphocyte.

★ **B-lymphocytes** produce **antibodies** which are proteins that attack antigens.

★ **T-lymphocytes** do not produce antibodies. Instead they bind with an antigen and destroy it.

Phagocytes in the blood engulf and destroy antigens. Some phagocytes pass through the walls of blood vessels and migrate through tissues to attack antigens that have entered the body through cuts or scratches. Their action causes an **inflammatory response** – swelling, redness and heat as the phagocytes destroy the invading antigens at the site of the infection. The diagram overleaf shows B-lymphocytes and phagocytes at work in the blood.

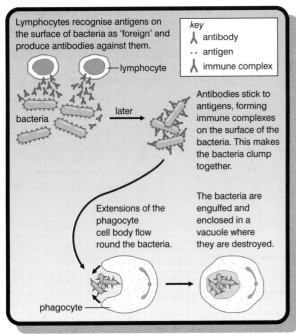

Lymphocytes recognise antigens on the surface of bacteria as 'foreign' and produce antibodies against them.

key
- ⋏ antibody
- ∴ antigen
- ⋏ immune complex

lymphocyte

bacteria

later

Antibodies stick to antigens, forming immune complexes on the surface of the bacteria. This makes the bacteria clump together.

Extensions of the phagocyte cell body flow round the bacteria.

The bacteria are engulfed and enclosed in a vacuole where they are destroyed.

phagocyte

B-lymphocytes produce antibodies which damage bacteria 'foreign' to the body (antigens). Phagocytes engulf the bacteria.

Diseases of the upper respiratory tract and lungs

Despite its filtering and cleaning mechanisms, the upper respiratory tract may become infected by disease-causing microorganisms. Infection of the

- throat (pharynx) is called **pharyngitis**
- voicebox (larynx) is called **laryngitis**
- windpipe (trachea) is called **tracheitis**
- bronchi and bronchioles is called **bronchitis**.

RESPIRATORY TRACT Page 72.

Pneumonia is an infection of the lungs caused by a particular type of bacterium. In pneumonia,

- Fluid collects in the lungs.

As a result, the surface area available for the absorption of oxygen is reduced.

As a result, the patient becomes breathless.

Pleurisy is an infection of the pleural membranes caused by a particular type of bacterium. In pleurisy,

- Infection makes the membranes rough.

As a result, there is pain when the membranes rub together.

Antibiotic drugs are used to treat pneumonia and pleurisy.

Smoking

Smoking cigarettes is a major cause of lung cancer and heart disease. Cigarette smoke is acidic and contains various substances harmful to health.

★ **Nicotine** is a powerful drug which increases the heart rate and blood pressure.

FACTS

★ **Carbon monoxide** is a poisonous gas which combines 300 times more readily with haemoglobin than oxygen does.

As a result, the level of oxygen in the blood is reduced.

★ **Tar** is a mixture of many compounds, some of which cause cancer (are **carcinogens**).

Some substances in cigarette smoke irritate the membrane lining the upper respiratory tract.

As a result, extra mucus (phlegm) forms in the trachea and bronchi.

As a result, the person may develop 'smoker's cough' in an attempt to remove the excess phlegm.

Other substances in cigarette smoke stop the cilia from beating.

As a result, particles and microorganisms enter the lungs.

As a result, the risk of infection is increased.

Emphysema is caused by repeated coughing, which destroys the walls of the alveoli.

As a result, the surface area available for the absorption of oxygen is reduced.

As a result, the person becomes breathless.

Lung cancer is caused by the carcinogens in tar. Abnormal cell division in lung tissue leads to the development of tumours (growths) which may be difficult to cure. Cancer cells may break away from the tumours and circulate in the blood to start **secondary** growths elsewhere in the body.

The smoking habit

Smoking cigarettes was fashionable in the early 1900s, and many people became smokers. Scientists soon suspected a link between smoking cigarettes and lung cancer.

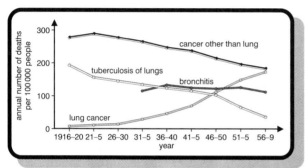

Deaths from lung cancer increased sharply in England and Wales from 1916 to 1960, which was the period when more and more people were smoking cigarettes. Other forms of lung disease were declining.

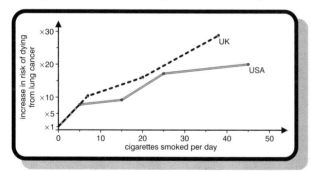

Studies have shown that the more cigarettes smoked, the greater is the risk of dying from lung cancer.

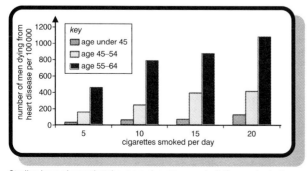

Studies have shown that the more cigarettes smoked, the greater is the risk of dying from heart disease.

Today there are fewer smokers than non-smokers in the United Kingdom. However, of the people who do smoke, there are many young people (especially girls). SMOKING IS A MUG'S GAME – DO NOT START!

REMEMBER – IF YOU DO SMOKE YOU CAN GIVE IT UP. Advice and help are available.

Drugs

Drugs are used to help in the fight against disease. For example,

★ **Antibiotics** are used to attack the different types of bacteria that cause disease.

★ **Analgesics** are drugs that reduce pain (painkillers).

Some drugs are highly **addictive** and may be **abused**. This means they are used for non-medical purposes.

Alcohol

Ethanol (the alcohol in beers, wine and spirits) depresses the activity of the nervous system. Small amounts affect the **cortex** of the brain which controls judgement. Large quantities affect the **motor cortex** which controls movement. Even more impairs memory. Drinking increasing amounts of alcohol affects other areas of the brain until it reaches brain centres that keep us alive. Death may follow.

Solvents

Glues, paints, nail varnish and cleaning fluids (dry cleaners) contain volatile solvents such as esters and

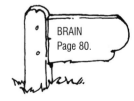

BRAIN Page 80.

ethanol. These are liquids in which other substances dissolve, and which readily produce a vapour at room temperature. Breathing them in gives a warm sense of well-being, but also produces dangerous disorientation. Long-term solvent abuse can damage the brain, kidneys and liver.

6

6.2 More about immunology

preview

preview

At the end of this section you will:
- understand the mechanism of the immune response
- be able to distinguish between B-cell lymphocytes and T-cell lymphocytes
- understand the basis of immunological memory
- be able to explain why tissue transplants are vulnerable to rejection.

Some definitions

★ **Immunology** is the study of processes that establish specific immunity in the body.

★ **Immunity** is the ability of an individual's immune system to destroy antigens, especially microorganisms and parasites that cause disease (pathogens).

★ The **immune system** consists of different categories of white blood cell – B-cell lymphocytes, T-cell lymphocytes and phagocytes – which destroy antigens.

Read (or re-read) Sections 5.5 and 6.1 to check up on antibodies, antigens, lymphocytes, phagocytes and pathogens.

The immune response and immunological memory

The body's immune response to a particular antigen occurs in two phases:

1 a **primary response** when an antigen first invades the body. The body takes a few days to produce antibodies (part of the **immune reaction**) against a first-time infection. The delay may allow symptoms of disease to develop if the antigen is a pathogen.

2 a **secondary response** should the same antigen invade the body again. The secondary response to the antigen is much quicker than the primary response because
- **memory cells** left over from the division of lymphocytes during the primary response recognise the antigen and quickly divide.

As a result of the rapidity of the secondary response, the immune reaction is almost immediate, destroying the antigen.

As a result, symptoms of the disease do not develop.

Memory cells specific for particular antigens prevent us from catching diseases like mumps and chickenpox more than once. The rapid secondary response destroys the pathogens before they make us ill.

Lymphocytes

Lymphocytes are the white blood cells that recognise and react to antigens. They originate in the **bone marrow**, a yellow fatty material that fills the hollow centre of the shafts of the long bones.

There are two categories of lymphocytes.

★ **B-cell lymphocytes** produce antibodies specific to the antigen that triggers their response.

★ **T-cell lymphocytes** do not produce antibodies but
- bind with an antigen and
- divide to form a variety of cell types that have different functions, for example **T-helper** cells control the production of antibodies by B-cell lymphocytes and **T-cytotoxic** cells destroy virus-infected cells.

Transplants and rejection

Tissue transplants help people recover from serious illnesses. The most frequent types of transplant are

- skin – treatment for burns
- kidney – treatment for kidney failure as an alternative to dialysis
- heart – treatment for heart failure.

The **donor** is the person from whom the tissue is taken. The **recipient** is the person who recieves the transplant.

Why are transplanted tissues vulnerable to rejection?

The antigens on the cell membranes of the donor are different from the antigens on the cell membranes of the recipient. The antigens are called **human lymphocyte antigens** (**HLA**).

As a result, the recipient's immune system mounts an immune response to the 'foreign' donor tissue.

As a result, T-cell lymphocytes and phagocytes invade the donor tissue.

As a result, the donor tissue is rejected and the transplant fails.

Different methods are used to reduce the chance of rejection.

★ **Identical twins** have identical genotypes. Their HLA antigens are therefore the same, preventing rejection if one twin donates tissue to the other.
★ **Tissue typing** identifies the different HLA antigens in the donor and recipient. Matching the HLA antigens between donor and recipient as closely as possible reduces the risk of rejection.
★ **Immunosuppressive drugs** prevent the recipient's T-cell lymphocytes from acting against the antigens in the transplanted tissue. **Cyclosporine** is one of the most effective immunosuppressive drugs.

6.3 Controlling the spread of disease

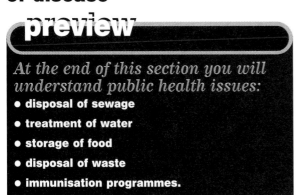

preview

At the end of this section you will understand public health issues:
● disposal of sewage
● treatment of water
● storage of food
● disposal of waste
● immunisation programmes.

Making the link

Good health depends not only on the treatment of disease, but also on preventing disease. Hygienic disposal of sewage and waste, the safe storage of food, and immunisation programmes are particularly important measures which control the spread of disease.

Disposal of sewage

On average a person produces 1.5 litres of urine and faeces each day. Urine and faeces are components of sewage; so too are industrial and household wastes and the water and grit that drain from roads and paths.

Untreated sewage is a health hazard. It contains microorganisms causing diseases such as cholera, typhoid, poliomyelitis and diphtheria. It also attracts insects which help to spread disease.

Other microorganisms help us treat sewage by breaking it down into harmless and even useful substances. This treatment occurs in sewage works. The sequence of processes is shown in the diagram overleaf.

Treatment of water

Four-fifths of the diseases in the Developing (Third) World are caused by people drinking dirty water. Providing water which is safe to drink is the single most effective measure for controlling the spread of disease. The process runs:

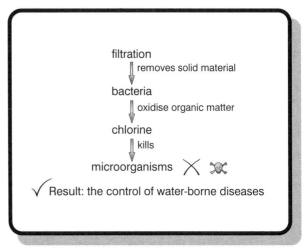

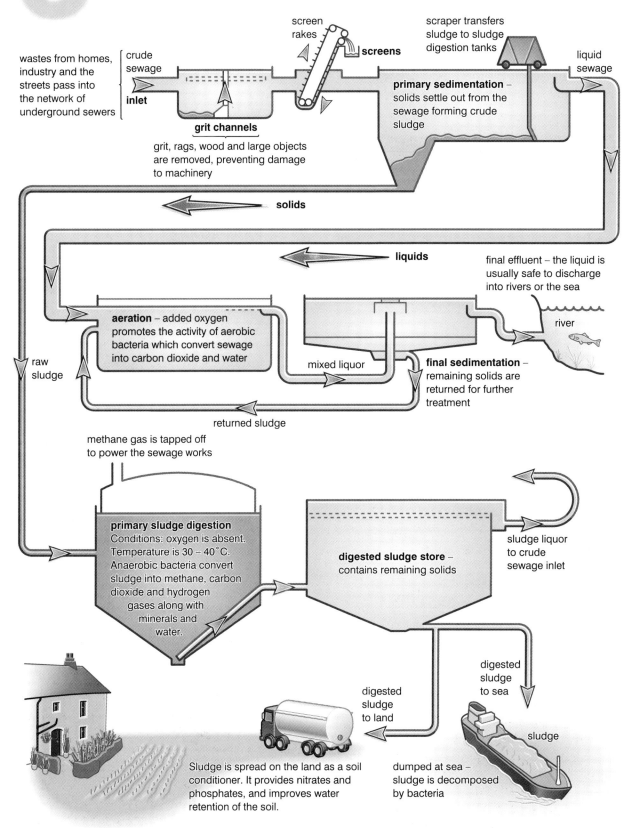

screen rakes

screens

scraper transfers sludge to sludge digestion tanks

liquid sewage

wastes from homes, industry and the streets pass into the network of underground sewers

crude sewage

inlet

primary sedimentation – solids settle out from the sewage forming crude sludge

grit channels

grit, rags, wood and large objects are removed, preventing damage to machinery

solids

liquids

final effluent – the liquid is usually safe to discharge into rivers or the sea

river

aeration – added oxygen promotes the activity of aerobic bacteria which convert sewage into carbon dioxide and water

mixed liquor

final sedimentation – remaining solids are returned for further treatment

raw sludge

returned sludge

methane gas is tapped off to power the sewage works

primary sludge digestion
Conditions: oxygen is absent. Temperature is 30 – 40°C. Anaerobic bacteria convert sludge into methane, carbon dioxide and hydrogen gases along with minerals and water.

digested sludge store – contains remaining solids

sludge liquor to crude sewage inlet

digested sludge to sea

digested sludge to land

sludge

Sludge is spread on the land as a soil conditioner. It provides nitrates and phosphates, and improves water retention of the soil.

dumped at sea – sludge is decomposed by bacteria

Treating sewage

Storage of food

Fungi and bacteria can easily come into contact with food, and some of them cause diseases. Methods of preserving food and preventing food-borne diseases include the following.

★ **Sterilisation** kills bacteria. Food is heated to a high temperature and then sealed in air-tight containers, such as tins.

★ **Pasteurisation** of milk and cheese means flash-heating the milk to 72 °C for 15 seconds, which kills most bacteria.

★ **Refrigeration** at a temperature between 0 °C and 5 °C stops bacteria from reproducing and slows their other activities.

★ **Freezing** at between −18 °C and −24 °C stops all bacterial activity.

★ **Drying** prevents bacteria reproducing.

★ **Ohmic heating** cooks and sterilises food by passing an electric current through it.

★ **Chemical preservatives** either stop the growth of bacteria, or kill them.

★ **Pickling** stops the growth of bacteria.

★ **Jam-making** preserves food in concentrated sugar solution. Bacteria lose water through osmosis and are killed.

OSMOSIS
Page 33.

★ **Smoking** food over burning wood or peat deposits substances that kill bacteria and moulds on the food.

★ **Irradiation** exposes food to γ-radiation, killing bacteria and moulds.

Food hygiene

Frozen food should be thawed before cooking unless the instructions say that the food can be cooked from frozen. It is especially important to thaw chicken and then cook it to a temperature of at least 68 °C, which kills bacteria, otherwise the centre of the carcass may not reach the 'safe' temperature. Chicken carcasses are often infected with *Salmonella* bacteria after slaughter. Someone who eats food contaminated with

Salmonella soon develops the symptoms of food poisoning, which include:

- fever
- pain
- vomiting
- diarrhoea.

The victim loses water and the body quickly dehydrates. Young children and elderly people are particularly vulnerable to the effects of food poisoning.

Disposal of waste

Insects are attracted by decomposing waste and may spread disease. Most household waste in the UK is therefore dumped into large holes in the ground. The operation is called **landfill**. Bacteria naturally present in the soil decompose the waste. When the hole has been filled, it is covered with soil and returned to agricultural use.

There are problems with landfill.

★ Decomposition of waste produces methane gas, which is inflammable. If the gas accumulates, it may explode. Some modern landfill sites pipe off the methane for industrial and domestic use as fuel.

★ Water percolating through the waste dissolves salts of lead, cadmium and copper. These heavy metals are very poisonous and may leak from landfill sites into domestic water supplies.

Other ways of disposing of waste include **incineration** and **recycling**.

Immunisation programmes

The action of lymphocytes and phagocytes against invading microorganisms in the body is called an **immune reaction** (see page 102). The responses are the components of an **active immunity** against disease. **Immunisation** promotes active immunity to a particular infection. A doctor or nurse gives a person an injection, or a substance to swallow. The substance injected or swallowed is a **vaccine** and the process of being immunised is called **immunisation** (or **vaccination**).

Vaccines are made from one of the following:

* dead microorganisms
* a weakened (**attenuated**) form of the microorganism, which is harmless
* a substance produced by the microorganism which does not cause disease
* genetically engineered microorganisms.

The vaccine contains antigens from the pathogen which stimulate the person's B-cell lymphocytes to produce antibodies. When the same active pathogen invades the body, the antibodies made in response to the vaccine destroy them. The active immunity produced by vaccines can protect a person from disease for a long time. **Booster** vaccinations keep up the level of antibodies and so maintain a person's immunity.

Children in the UK are immunised against several diseases that used to cause many deaths: diphtheria, tetanus, whooping cough, poliomyelitis, tuberculosis and German measles.

6.4 Fighting infectious diseases

preview

At the end of this section you will:

* be able to distinguish between antisepsis and asepsis
* know that drugs are used to attack different pathogens
* understand how pathogens develop resistance to drugs
* be able to explain why mosquitoes are vectors of different diseases, especially malaria.

★ **Remember** that organisms that cause disease are called **pathogens**.

★ Diseases are said to be **infectious** if the organisms can be passed from one person to another.

DISEASES
Page 98.

Antiseptics, disinfectants and aseptic surgery

Antiseptics and disinfectants are chemicals that we use outside the body to attack microorganisms which might otherwise cause disease.

★ **Antiseptics** stop microorganisms from multiplying. They can be used to swab a wound or before an injection to clean the area of skin where the hypodermic needle is to be inserted.

★ **Disinfectants** are usually stronger than antiseptics. They kill microorganisms and are used to keep surfaces such as lavatory bowls and kitchen tables free from microorganisms.

Aseptic surgery aims to prevent microorganisms from infecting a wound. The following procedures keep the operating theatre as sterile as possible.

* Sterilised gowns and gloves are worn by surgeons and their assistants.
* Air entering the operating theatre is filtered.
* Equipment, furniture and surfaces are designed to be easy to clean.

Chemotherapy

The word **chemotherapy** means using drugs to combat pathogens. **Antibiotic** drugs attack bacteria which cause disease:

* **bactericides** such as penicillin kill bacteria
* **bacteristats** such as tetracycline prevent bacteria from multiplying.

The diagram at the top of the opposite page shows how different antibiotics affect bacteria.

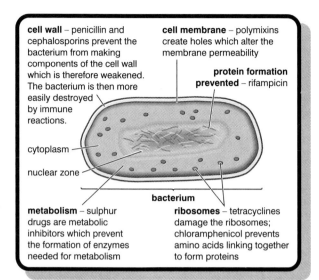

cell wall – penicillin and cephalosporins prevent the bacterium from making components of the cell wall which is therefore weakened. The bacterium is then more easily destroyed by immune reactions.

cytoplasm

nuclear zone

cell membrane – polymixins create holes which alter the membrane permeability

protein formation prevented – rifampicin

bacterium

metabolism – sulphur drugs are metabolic inhibitors which prevent the formation of enzymes needed for metabolism

ribosomes – tetracyclines damage the ribosomes; chloramphenicol prevents amino acids linking together to form proteins

Antibiotic drugs at work. Ribosomes are the places within the cell where proteins are made.

Fact file

Three scientists were involved in the discovery and development of penicillin.

★ In 1928 **Alexander Fleming** noticed that the mould *Penicillium notatum* killed bacteria. He isolated the active substance and called it **penicillin**.

★ In 1938 **Howard Florey** and **Ernst Chain** began to develop methods to produce enough penicillin for clinical trials.

★ By 1944 penicillin was in large-scale production, following the move of production from Britain to the USA at the onset of the Second World War.

Resistance

Bacteria can become **resistant** to a particular antibiotic, and that antibiotic becomes less effective for the treatment of disease.

★ The dosage of a drug to which bacteria are becoming resistant has to be gradually increased as symptoms continue.

As a result, the drug becomes increasingly inefficient as resistance develops.

As a result, the drug may become poisonous to the patient.

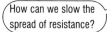

How can we slow the spread of resistance?

Answer

★ Avoid using antibiotics by practising good hygiene to prevent the spread of infection.

★ Use antibiotics sparingly when drugs are needed to treat infection.

★ Finish a prescribed course of antibiotics.

★ Reduce the antibiotics given to farm animals.

How do doctors deal with resistant infections?

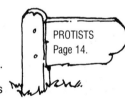

Answer

★ Different types of antibiotic are prescribed to treat different diseases, and drugs are switched if resistance develops.

★ Research scientists work continually to develop new antibiotics.

However, the race to develop new drugs as bacteria develop resistance to existing ones is close. The race is an example of the 'Red Queen Effect'. Find out what the Red Queen says to Alice in *Through the Looking Glass* by Lewis Carroll.

Mosquitoes and malaria

The transmission of malaria involves these steps:

★ *Plasmodium* species are protists that cause human malaria. The parasites infect liver cells and red blood cells.

PROTISTS Page 14.

★ Female *Anopheles* mosquitoes feed on human blood.

★ The mosquitoes suck up the parasites in the red blood cells when they feed on infected people.

★ A mosquito that has fed on infected people transmits the parasite to new human hosts when it feeds on them.

The diagram overleaf shows the relationship beween parasite, mosquito and people.

• A **host** is a person who is infected with a *Plasmodium* parasite.

• A **vector** transmits the disease. The female mosquito is the vector for malaria because it transmits the parasite from host to new host.

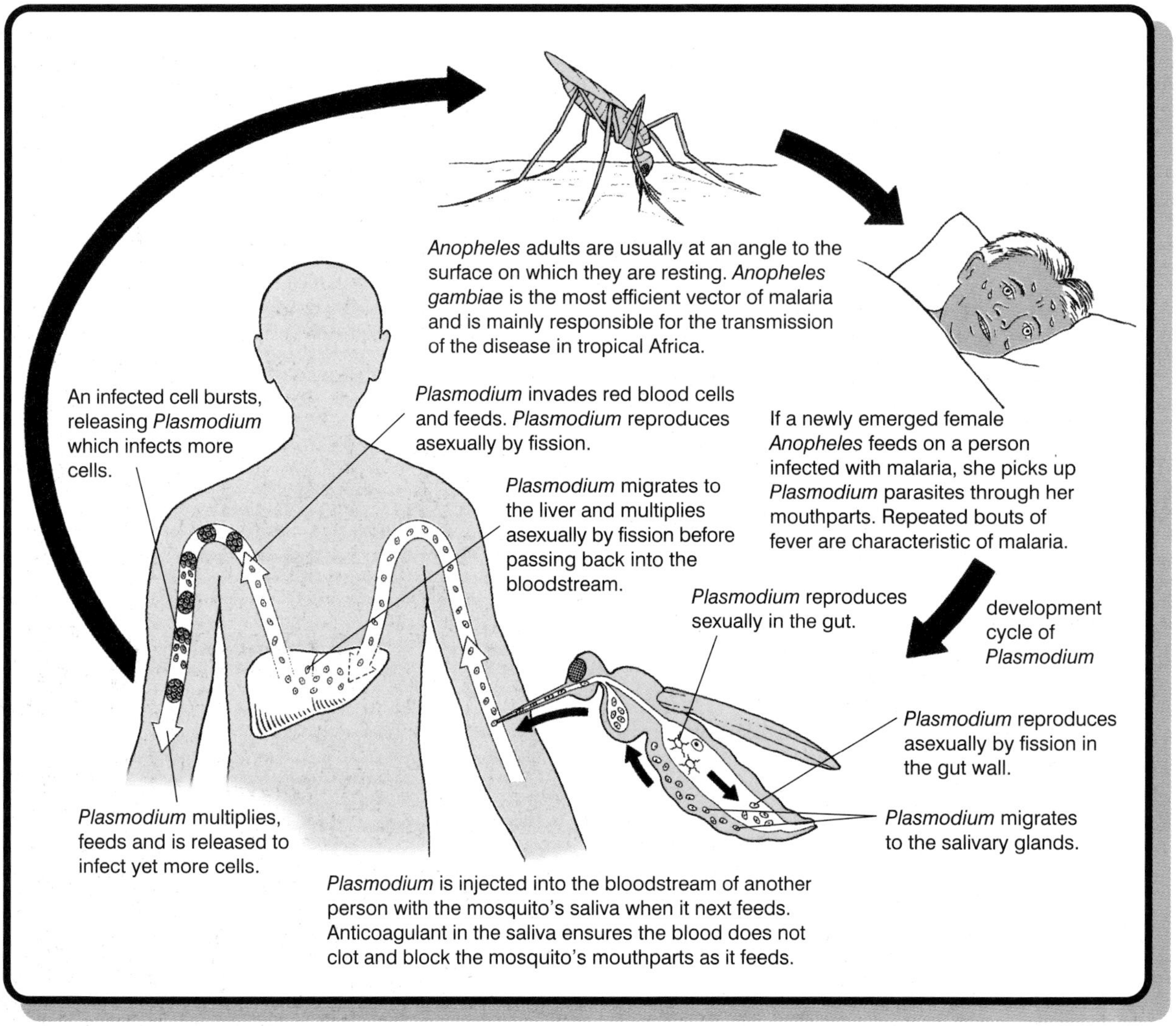
Anopheles adults are usually at an angle to the surface on which they are resting. *Anopheles gambiae* is the most efficient vector of malaria and is mainly responsible for the transmission of the disease in tropical Africa.
An infected cell bursts, releasing *Plasmodium* which infects more cells.
Plasmodium invades red blood cells and feeds. *Plasmodium* reproduces asexually by fission.
If a newly emerged female *Anopheles* feeds on a person infected with malaria, she picks up *Plasmodium* parasites through her mouthparts. Repeated bouts of fever are characteristic of malaria.
Plasmodium migrates to the liver and multiplies asexually by fission before passing back into the bloodstream.
Plasmodium reproduces sexually in the gut.
development cycle of *Plasmodium*
Plasmodium reproduces asexually by fission in the gut wall.
Plasmodium migrates to the salivary glands.
Plasmodium multiplies, feeds and is released to infect yet more cells.
Plasmodium is injected into the bloodstream of another person with the mosquito's saliva when it next feeds. Anticoagulant in the saliva ensures the blood does not clot and block the mosquito's mouthparts as it feeds.

Transmission of the malaria parasite

Treatment and prevention of malaria

Fighting malaria depends on

★ **Treatment:**
- drugs like quinine, chloroquine and quinacrine destroy the parasite in the host
- vaccines inhibit different stages in the parasite's life cycle.

★ **Destroying the mosquito vector:**
- draining marshes, ponds and ditches prevents the female mosquito from laying eggs, and the eggs from developing into larvae
- spraying insecticides onto the water's surface kills mosquito larvae and pupae
- introducing fish which eat mosquito larvae (an example of **biological control**).

★ **Preventing contact between mosquitoes and people**
- bed nets soaked with insecticide protect people while they are asleep
- chemical repellant sprayed on the skin and clothes deters mosquitoes from landing on the body.

round-up

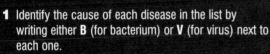

How much have you improved?
Work out your improvement index on pages 138–9.

1 Identify the cause of each disease in the list by writing either **B** (for bacterium) or **V** (for virus) next to each one.
cholera AIDS syphilis 'flu pneumonia [5]

2 List the different types of white blood cell. Explain the role of each type of cell in the defence of the body against disease. [6]

3 Match each of the body's natural defences against disease in column A with its correct description in column B. [5]

A defences	B descriptions
mucus	a substance which kills bacteria and fungi on the skin
lysozyme	destroy antigens
hydrochloric acid	traps particles and bacteria which are removed from the body by cilia
antibodies	destroys bacteria, preventing infection of the eye
sebum	kills bacteria on food

4 How many glasses of table wine contain the same amount of alcohol (ethanol) as $2\frac{1}{2}$ pints of beer? [1]

5 Distinguish between the following terms.
a) antibiotics and analgesics [2]
b) B-lymphocytes and T-lymphocytes [4]
c) lung cancer and emphysema [2]

6 Identify the substances in cigarette smoke which are harmful to health. Briefly explain why they are harmful. [6]

7 Distinguish between the following terms.
a) primary immune response and secondary immune response [5]
b) lymphocytes and phagocytes [9]
c) T-helper cells and T-cytotoxic cells [3]

8 Briefly explain why
a) tissue typing and immunosuppressive drugs help prevent rejection by the recipient of transplanted tissue [4]
b) the transplantation of tissue between identical twins carries the least risk of rejection. [2]

9 Distinguish between the following pairs of terms.
a) vaccine and vaccination [3]
b) refrigeration and freezing [2]
c) activated sludge process and trickling filter process [4]

10 How do booster vaccinations help to maintain a person's immunity to disease? [1]

11 Why are the symptoms of vomiting and diarrhoea associated with food poisoning a serious risk to health? [2]

12 Distinguish between the following terms.
a) host and vector [4]
b) bactericides and bacteristats [4]
c) chemotherapy and resistance [4]

13 Briefly explain the precautions which can be taken to slow the development of bacterial resistance to different drugs. [6]

14 List the methods available for the treatment and prevention of malaria. [9]

Well done if you've improved. Don't worry if you haven't. Take a break and try again.

Inheritance and evolution

7

How much do you already know?
Work out your score on page 139.

7.1 Reproduction

preview

At the end of this section you will:

- **know that reproduction gives rise to offspring**
- **understand that sexual reproduction gives rise to variation in offspring and that asexual reproduction gives rise to identical offspring**
- **be able to identify the components of the human reproductive system**
- **know how sexual reproduction occurs in humans and in flowering plants.**

Test yourself

1 The diagram shows the reproductive system of a man. Name parts A–E.

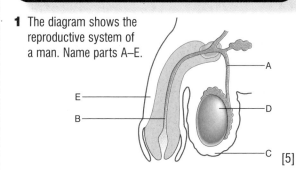

[5]

2 Match each structure in column **A** with its correct description in column **B**.

A structures	B descriptions
corm	a horizontal stem running above ground
runner	a short, swollen underground stem
tuber	a large underground bud
bulb	a swelling at the end of a rhizome

[4]

3 In humans, the gene for brown eyes (**B**) is dominant to the gene for blue eyes (**b**).
  a) Using the symbols **B** and **b**, state the genotypes of the children that could be born from a marriage between a heterozygous father and a blue-eyed mother. [2]
  b) State whether the children are brown eyed or blue eyed. [2]

4 Why are acquired characteristics not inherited? [3]

5 List the different sources of variation in living things. [6]

6 Why does sexual reproduction produce much more genetic variation than asexual reproduction? [5]

7 Distinguish between the following terms.
  a) ancestors and descendants [1]
  b) adaptation and extinction [2]
  c) evolution and natural selection [3]

8 How are fossils formed? [4]

Sexual or asexual?

Reproduction passes genetic material on from parents to their offspring. There are two types of reproduction.

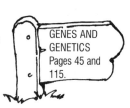

GENES AND GENETICS
Pages 45 and 115.

In **sexual reproduction**, *two* parents (male and female) produce sex cells called **gametes**. Gametes are formed by **meiosis**. The male gametes are **sperm**. The female gametes are **eggs**. The sperm and egg fuse – this is called **fertilisation**. The fertilised egg cell is called a **zygote**. The zygote divides repeatedly, producing a ball of cells called an **embryo** which develops into the new individual. The offspring formed by sexual reproduction inherit genes from each parent, and are genetically *different* from one another and from their parents. In other words, they show **variation**.

Dear Student

    IMPORTANT ANNOUNCEMENT
Topic 3.3 about meiosis and mitosis is **REALLY REALLY** important to your understanding of sexual and asexual reproduction.

    Luv Owl

In **asexual reproduction**, *one* parent divides by **mitosis** to produce daughter cells which form new individuals. These offspring are genetically *identical* to one another and to their parent because DNA replicates exact copies of itself during mitosis.

Sexual reproduction in humans and flowering plants

How much do you recall about the structure of the reproductive organs in flowering plants and humans? Remember that **flowers** are shoots which are specialised for reproduction. The **genitalia** are the visible parts of the human reproductive system. The Mind Map for reproduction is shown overleaf. The numbers on the Mind Map refer to the checklist below.

Checklist for reproduction

1 ★ The testes hang down between the legs.

As a result, the testes are protected from injury.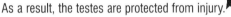

★ The position of the testes keeps them about 3 °C lower than body temperature.

As a result, sperm develop properly in the slightly cooler conditions.

★ A woman's genitalia cover and protect the opening to the rest of the reproductive system inside her body.

MENSTRUAL CYCLE Page 87.

2 ★ A fertilised egg is called a **zygote**. It develops into a new individual. The sequence reads:

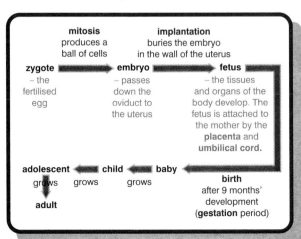

mitosis produces a ball of cells	implantation buries the embryo in the wall of the uterus	
zygote ➡	**embryo** ➡	**fetus**
– the fertilised egg	– passes down the oviduct to the uterus	– the tissues and organs of the body develop. The fetus is attached to the mother by the **placenta** and **umbilical cord.**
adolescent ⬅	**child** ⬅ **baby**	
grows	grows grows	**birth** after 9 months' development (**gestation** period)
adult		

The development of the zygote

★ In humans, pregnancy usually results in the birth of only one baby. However, sometimes **twins** are born.

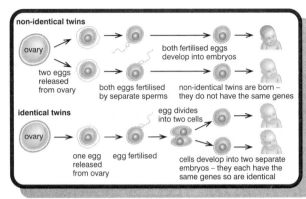

Producing twins

3 ★ **Contraception** aims to prevent pregnancy by
- preventing sperm from reaching the egg, or
- preventing eggs from being produced, or
- preventing the fertilised egg from developing in the uterus.

4 ★ In flowering plants, sexual reproduction involves **pollination**, **fertilisation** and the formation of **fruits** and **seeds**. The sequence reads:

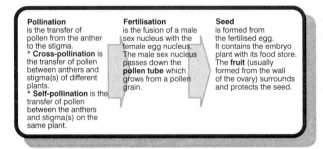

Pollination is the transfer of pollen from the anther to the stigma. * **Cross-pollination** is the transfer of pollen between anthers and stigma(s) of different plants. * **Self-pollination** is the transfer of pollen between the anthers and stigma(s) on the same plant.	**Fertilisation** is the fusion of a male sex nucleus with the female egg nucleus. The male sex nucleus passes down the **pollen tube** which grows from a pollen grain.	**Seed** is formed from the fertilised egg. It contains the embryo plant with its food store. The **fruit** (usually formed from the wall of the ovary) surrounds and protects the seed.

★ Flowers are adapted for pollination.
- **Insect-pollinated** flowers are brightly coloured and produce nectar and scent to attract insect visitors.
- **Wind-pollinated** flowers are often a dull colour and are adapted to distribute large quantities of pollen far and wide.

★ Fruits and seeds are adapted for distribution by either animals or wind.
- **Spines** and **hooks** attach the fruit to passing animals.
- Animals are attracted to feed on **brightly coloured** fruits. The seeds are protected from the digestive juices in the animal's intestine, and eventually pass out in the animal's faeces.
- **Parachutes** and **wings** increase the surface area of fruits, helping them travel in the wind.

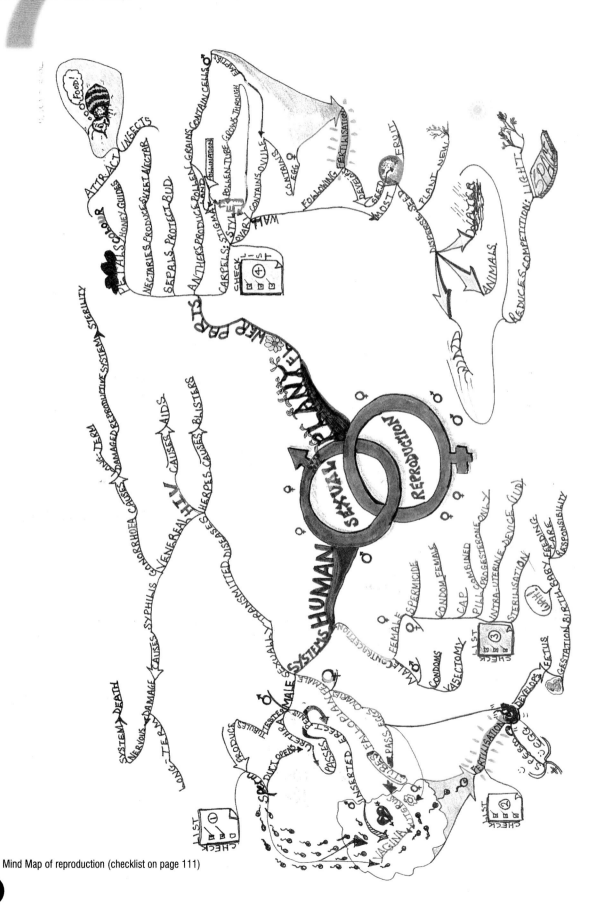

Mind Map of reproduction (checklist on page 111)

7.2 Asexual reproduction in plants

preview

At the end of this section you will:

- be able to identify the organs of asexual reproduction in flowering plants

- know that cuttings, graftings and micropropagation are used by farmers and gardeners to produce many identical plants

- understand that asexual reproduction preserves desirable characteristics and so guarantees plant quality.

Remember that asexual reproduction gives rise to **genetically identical** individuals, because DNA replicates during mitosis. This process passes on exact copies of the parent's genetic material to the daughter cells.

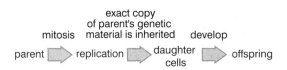

Remember

★ Genetically identical individuals are called **clones** (see page 37).

Vegetative reproduction

Different parts of flowering plants can reproduce asexually. They are called the **vegetative parts** and are formed from the **root**, **leaf** or **stem**.

Asexual reproduction in flowering plants is sometimes called **vegetative reproduction**. Since the new plants come from a single parent, they are genetically the same and are therefore **clones**.

The vegetative parts of plants store food. The stored food is used for the development of the new plant(s). We sometimes eat these food storage organs as vegetables, for example, potatoes.

The concept map for **asexual reproduction in plants** is shown overleaf. It is your revision guide, so study it carefully.

Artificial vegetative reproduction

Gardeners and farmers need to produce fresh stocks of plants that have desirable characteristics such as disease resistance, colour of fruit or shape of flower. The diagram below shows how they use vegetative propagation.

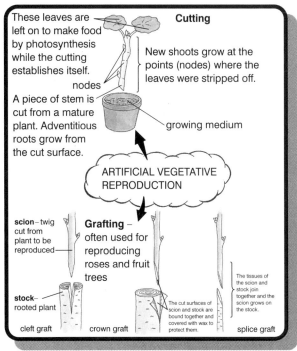

Exploiting vegetative reproduction

Micropropagation is used to grow plants from small pieces, using a technique called **tissue culture**.

★ Small fragments of plant tissue are grown in a liquid or gel that contains all the necessary ingredients.

★ Conditions are sterile.

   As a result, the new plants are free of disease.

★ The temperature is carefully controlled.

All the plants grown from pieces of one parent plant will be genetically identical. They are clones. The advantages are that the plants

- are healthy
- are the same
- retain the desirable characteristics of the parent plant.

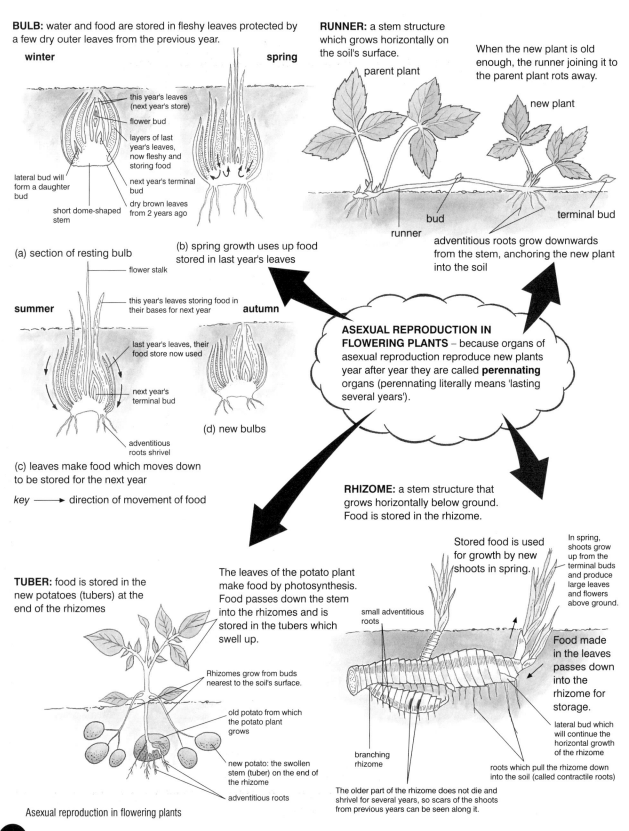

BULB: water and food are stored in fleshy leaves protected by a few dry outer leaves from the previous year.

winter

- this year's leaves (next year's store)
- flower bud
- layers of last year's leaves, now fleshy and storing food
- lateral bud will form a daughter bud
- next year's terminal bud
- short dome-shaped stem
- dry brown leaves from 2 years ago

spring

(a) section of resting bulb

(b) spring growth uses up food stored in last year's leaves

summer

- flower stalk
- this year's leaves storing food in their bases for next year
- last year's leaves, their food store now used
- next year's terminal bud
- adventitious roots shrivel

autumn

(d) new bulbs

(c) leaves make food which moves down to be stored for the next year

key ⟶ direction of movement of food

RUNNER: a stem structure which grows horizontally on the soil's surface.

- parent plant

When the new plant is old enough, the runner joining it to the parent plant rots away.

- new plant
- runner
- bud
- terminal bud

adventitious roots grow downwards from the stem, anchoring the new plant into the soil

ASEXUAL REPRODUCTION IN FLOWERING PLANTS – because organs of asexual reproduction reproduce new plants year after year they are called **perennating** organs (perennating literally means 'lasting several years').

TUBER: food is stored in the new potatoes (tubers) at the end of the rhizomes

The leaves of the potato plant make food by photosynthesis. Food passes down the stem into the rhizomes and is stored in the tubers which swell up.

- Rhizomes grow from buds nearest to the soil's surface.
- old potato from which the potato plant grows
- new potato: the swollen stem (tuber) on the end of the rhizome
- adventitious roots

Asexual reproduction in flowering plants

RHIZOME: a stem structure that grows horizontally below ground. Food is stored in the rhizome.

Stored food is used for growth by new shoots in spring.

In spring, shoots grow up from the terminal buds and produce large leaves and flowers above ground.

- small adventitious roots

Food made in the leaves passes down into the rhizome for storage.

- lateral bud which will continue the horizontal growth of the rhizome
- branching rhizome
- roots which pull the rhizome down into the soil (called contractile roots)

The older part of the rhizome does not die and shrivel for several years, so scars of the shoots from previous years can be seen along it.

7.3 Monohybrid inheritance

preview

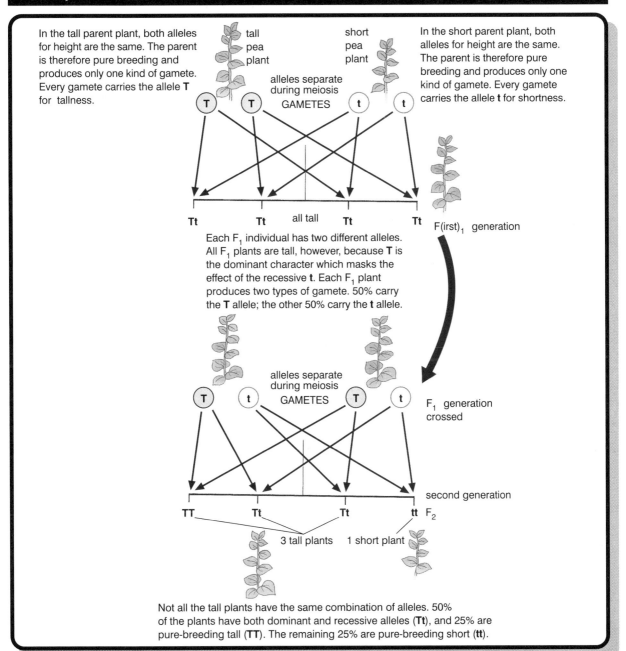

In the tall parent plant, both alleles for height are the same. The parent is therefore pure breeding and produces only one kind of gamete. Every gamete carries the allele **T** for tallness.

tall pea plant   short pea plant

In the short parent plant, both alleles for height are the same. The parent is therefore pure breeding and produces only one kind of gamete. Every gamete carries the allele **t** for shortness.

alleles separate during meiosis

T   **T**   GAMETES   **t**   **t**

Tt   **Tt**   all tall   **Tt**   **Tt** $F(irst)_1$ generation

Each F_1 individual has two different alleles. All F_1 plants are tall, however, because **T** is the dominant character which masks the effect of the recessive **t**. Each F_1 plant produces two types of gamete. 50% carry the **T** allele; the other 50% carry the **t** allele.

alleles separate during meiosis

T   **t**   GAMETES   **T**   **t** F_1 generation crossed

second generation

TT   **Tt**   **Tt**   **tt** F_2

3 tall plants   1 short plant

Not all the tall plants have the same combination of alleles. 50% of the plants have both dominant and recessive alleles (**Tt**), and 25% are pure-breeding tall (**TT**). The remaining 25% are pure-breeding short (**tt**).

How alleles controlling a characteristic (height) pass from one generation to the next

Fact file

Gregor Mendel was a monk who lived in the Augustinian monastery at the town of Brünn (now Brno in the Czech Republic). He observed the inheritance of different characteristics in the garden pea, and reported the results of his experiments in 1865. The work established the basis of modern genetics.

The vocabulary of genetics

★ **monohybrid inheritance** – the processes by which a single characteristic is passed from parents to offspring, for example flower colour or eye colour

★ **pure breeding** – characteristics that breed true, appearing unchanged generation after generation

★ **parental generation** (symbol **P**) – individuals that are pure breeding for a characteristic

★ **first filial generation** (symbol F_1) – the offspring produced by a parental generation

★ **second filial generation** (symbol F_2) – the offspring produced by crossing members of the first filial generation

★ **gene** – a length of DNA which codes for the whole of one protein

GENES
Page 45.

★ **allele** – one of a pair of genes that control a particular characteristic

★ **homozygote** – an individual with identical alleles controlling a particular characteristic. Individuals that are pure breeding for a particular characteristic are **homozygous** for that characteristic

★ **heterozygote** – an individual with different alleles controlling a particular characteristic

★ **expressed** – a gene is expressed when a protein is produced from the activity of the gene

★ **dominant** - any characteristic that appears in the F_1 offspring of a cross between pure-breeding parents with contrasting characteristics, such as tallness and shortness in pea plants, *or* any characteristic expressed by an allele in preference to the form of the characteristic controlled by the allele's partner

★ **recessive** – any characteristic present in the parental generation that misses the F_1 generation but reappears in the F_2 generation, *or* any characteristic of an allele that is not expressed because the form of the characteristic of the allele's partner is expressed in preference, *or* any characteristic of an allele that is only expressed in the absence of the allele's dominant partner

★ **genotype** – the genetic make-up (all of the genes) of an individual

★ **phenotype** – the outward appearance of an individual; the result of those genes of the genotype which are actively expressing characteristics.

Some rules of genetics

★ Paired genes controlling a particular characteristic are called alleles.

★ Letters are used to symbolise alleles.

★ A capital letter is used to symbolise the dominant member of a pair of alleles.

★ A small letter is used to symbolise the recessive member of a pair of alleles.

★ The letter used to symbolise the recessive allele is the same letter as that for the dominant allele.

A monohybrid cross

T is used to symbolise the allele that produces tallness in pea plants, and **t** is used to symbolise the allele that produces shortness. The diagram on the left sets out the results of crosses between tall and short pea plants. Other contrasting characteristics of the pea plant such as seed shape (round or wrinkled), flower colour (purple or white) and pod shape (smooth or wrinkled) are inherited in a similar way.

Inheritance of sex

The photograph shows the chromosomes that determine the sex of a person. The larger chromosome is the **X** chromosome; the smaller chromosome is the **Y** chromosome. The body cells of a woman carry two X chromosomes; those of a man carry an X chromosome and a Y chromosome.

![Human sex chromosomes]

Human sex chromosomes

The diagram below shows how a person's sex is inherited. Notice that

- a baby's sex depends on whether the egg is fertilised by a sperm carrying an X chromosome or one carrying a Y chromosome
- the birth of (almost) equal numbers of girls and boys is governed by the production of equal numbers of X and Y sperms at meiosis.

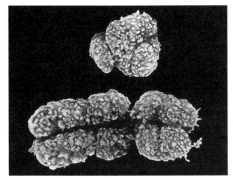

Inheritance of sex in humans

Sex-linked inheritance

Characteristics controlled by alleles situated on the sex chromosomes are said to be **sex-linked** characteristics. The disease **haemophilia** is an example. The diagram shows what happens.

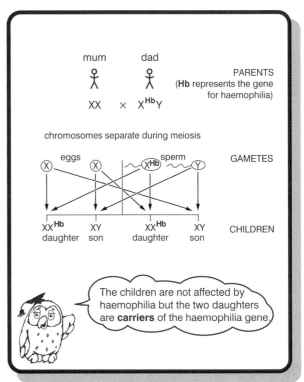

The outcome when a man affected by haemophilia becomes a father

The outcome when a woman who is a carrier of the haemophilia allele becomes a mother

7.4 Variation

preview

At the end of this section you will:
- **understand the difference between continuous variation and discontinuous variation**
- **be able to identify the sources of variation**
- **know that variation is either inherited or acquired.**

Genetic and environmental variation

Look closely at your family, friends and classmates. Notice the differently coloured hair and eyes, and the differently shaped faces. We all show **variations** in the different characteristics that make up our physical appearance (**phenotype**).

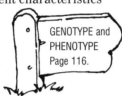
GENOTYPE and PHENOTYPE Page 116.

Variation arises from **genetic** causes.

Sexual reproduction (see pages 111–12) involves the fusion of the nucleus of a **sperm** with the nucleus of the **egg**. The fertilisation recombines the genetic material from each parent in new ways within the **zygote**.

Mutations arise as a result of mistakes in the **replication** of DNA (see page 46). Occasionally the wrong base adds to the growing strand of DNA, making the new DNA slightly different from the original. **Ionising radiation** and some **chemicals** increase the probability of gene mutation.

★ Ionising radiation strips electrons from matter exposed to it (ionises the atoms). Emissions from radioactive substances are ionising radiations. They may cause mutations by damaging DNA directly, or by generating highly active components of molecules called **free radicals** which cause the damage indirectly.

★ Chemicals such as the **carcinogens** (substances that cause cancer) in tobacco may lead to mutations of the genes that normally inhibit cell division.

As a result, cell division runs out of control and a cancer develops.

★ **Crossing over** during **meiosis** exchanges a segment of one chromosome (and the genes it carries) with the corresponding segment of its homologous chromosome.

As a result, the sex cells produced by meiosis have a different combination of genes from the parent cell.

Variations that arise from genetic causes are inherited from parents by their offspring, who pass them on to their offspring, and so on from generation to generation. Inherited variation is the raw material on which **natural selection** acts, resulting in **evolution**.

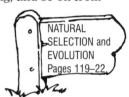
NATURAL SELECTION and EVOLUTION Pages 119–22.

Variation also arises from **environmental** causes. Here, 'environmental' means all the external influences affecting an organism, for example:

★ **Nutrients** in the food we eat and minerals that plants absorb in solution through the roots. In many countries, children are now taller and heavier, age for age, than they were 50 years ago because of improved diet and standards of living.

★ **Drugs**, which may have a serious effect on appearance. **Thalidomide** was given to pregnant women in the 1960s to prevent them feeling sick and help them sleep. The drug can affect the development of the fetus and some women who were prescribed thalidomide gave birth to seriously deformed children.

★ **Temperature** affects the rate of enzyme-controlled chemical reactions. For example, warmth increases the rate of photosynthesis and improves the rate of growth of plants kept under glass.

★ **Physical training** uses muscles more than normal, increasing their size and power. Weightlifters develop bulging muscles as they train for their sport.

Variations that arise from environmental causes are *not* inherited, because the sex cells are not affected. Instead the characteristics are said to be **acquired**. The fact that the weightlifter has developed bulging muscles does not mean that his or her children will have bulging muscles – unless they take up weightlifting as well! Because variations as a result of acquired characteristics are not inherited, they do not affect evolution.

Continuous and discontinuous variation

The variations shown by some characteristics are spread over a range of measurements. All intermediate forms of a characteristic are possible between one extreme and the other. We say that the characteristic shows **continuous variation**. The height of a population is an example of continuous variation, as shown.

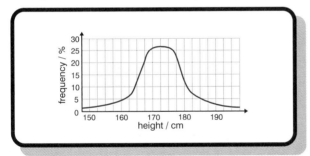

Variation in the height of the adult human population – an example of continuous variation

Other characteristics do not show a continuous trend in variation from one extreme to another. They show categories of the characteristic without any intermediate forms. The ability to roll the tongue is an example – you can either do it or you can't. There are no half-rollers! We say that the characteristic shows **discontinuous variation**.

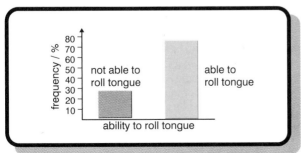

Ability to roll the tongue – an example of discontinuous variation

7.5 Evolution preview

At the end of this section you will:

- **know that the British naturalist Charles Darwin was the first person to explain how species can evolve**

- **understand Darwin's evidence showing that evolution occurs, and that natural selection is the mechanism of evolution**

- **be able to interpret examples of evolution in action**

- **know that fossils give a record of organisms that have become extinct.**

Fact file – Darwin

★ Charles Darwin (1809–82) was a keen British naturalist who abandoned medicine at Edinburgh and studied theology at Cambridge. His world voyage on HMS *Beagle* (1831–6) provided much of the evidence that

- organisms **evolve** and that
- **natural selection** is the mechanism of evolution.

It was another 20 years before he published these proposals in his book *The Origin of Species*.

The process of evolution

Present-day living things are descended from ancestors that have changed through thousands of generations. The process of change is called **evolution**. The concept map for evolution is shown overleaf. It shows that other people's ideas influenced Darwin's thinking on how species can evolve. The numbers on the concept map refer to the checklist of points on page 121. The concept map and its checklist are your revision guide to evolution.

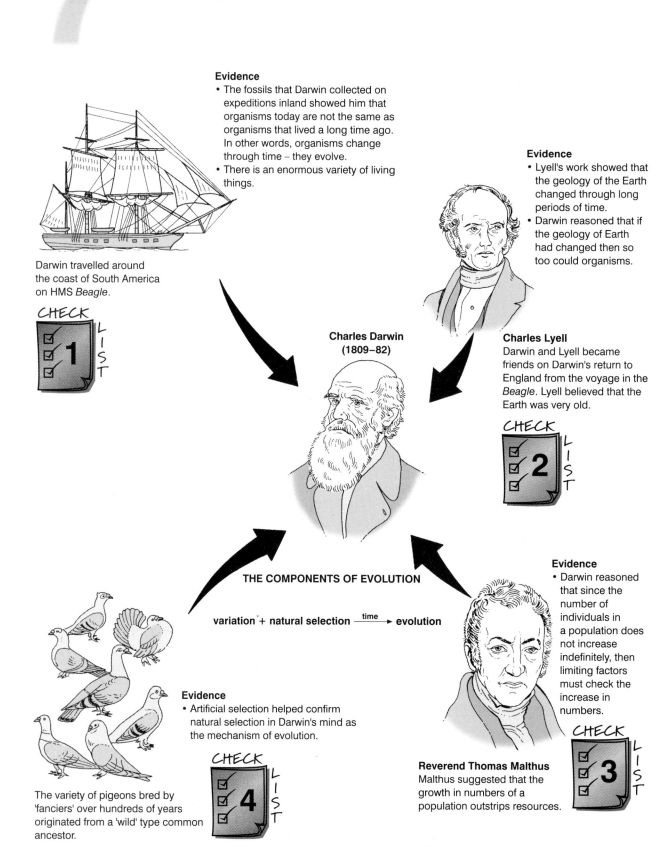

Evidence
- The fossils that Darwin collected on expeditions inland showed him that organisms today are not the same as organisms that lived a long time ago. In other words, organisms change through time – they evolve.
- There is an enormous variety of living things.

Evidence
- Lyell's work showed that the geology of the Earth changed through long periods of time.
- Darwin reasoned that if the geology of Earth had changed then so too could organisms.

Darwin travelled around the coast of South America on HMS *Beagle*.

CHECK **1** LIST

Charles Darwin (1809–82)

Charles Lyell
Darwin and Lyell became friends on Darwin's return to England from the voyage in the *Beagle*. Lyell believed that the Earth was very old.

CHECK **2** LIST

THE COMPONENTS OF EVOLUTION

variation + natural selection —time→ evolution

Evidence
- Darwin reasoned that since the number of individuals in a population does not increase indefinitely, then limiting factors must check the increase in numbers.

Evidence
- Artificial selection helped confirm natural selection in Darwin's mind as the mechanism of evolution.

CHECK **4** LIST

Reverend Thomas Malthus
Malthus suggested that the growth in numbers of a population outstrips resources.

CHECK **3** LIST

The variety of pigeons bred by 'fanciers' over hundreds of years originated from a 'wild' type common ancestor.

How Darwin arrived at a theory of evolution through natural selection (checklist opposite)

Checklist for evolution

1 A survey of the South American coast was among the tasks undertaken by the crew of HMS *Beagle* during its world voyage. At that time Darwin took over as the ship's naturalist. He

- collected **fossils** and specimens of plants and animals on expeditions inland
- noticed that one type of organism gave way to another as the *Beagle* sailed around the coast of South America
- observed that the animals along the Pacific coast of South America were different from those along the Atlantic coast
- compared the wildlife of the Galapagos Islands with the wildlife of the South American mainland, noting the differences between similar species.

The variety of species that Darwin discovered on his expeditions in South America and the Galapagos Islands convinced him that species change through time; that is, they **evolve**.

2 The famous geologist Charles Lyell (1797–1875) believed that

- Earth's rocks are very old
- natural forces produce continuous geological change during the course of Earth's history
- fossils can be used to date rocks
- the fossil record was laid down over hundreds of millions of years.

Darwin read Lyell's books.

As a result, Darwin reasoned that if rocks have changed slowly over long periods of time, living things might have a similar history.

3 In 1798 the Reverend Thomas Malthus wrote *An Essay on the Principle of Population*. He stated that a population would increase in number indefinitely unless kept in check by shortages of resources such as food and living space. Darwin read the essay in 1838 and reasoned that in nature a 'struggle for existence' must occur. In modern language we say that organisms **compete** for resources in limited supply.

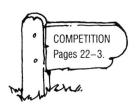

COMPETITION
Pages 22–3.

4 For centuries we have selected animals and plants for their desirable characteristics, and bred from them. This is called **artificial selection**. For example, dogs have been bred for shape, size and coat colour, resulting in a wide variety of breeds. Darwin investigated the work of breeders of animals and plants, and added to his experience by breeding pigeons. He reasoned that if artificial selection produced change in domestic animals and plants, then natural selection should have the same effect on wildlife.

Fact file – age of the Earth

★ Evidence suggests that Earth was formed about 4500 million years ago and that very simple forms of life first appeared around 4000 million years ago.

The checklist above sets out the different components which were the key to Darwin's understanding of how species evolve.

Variation: Darwin's work during the voyage of HMS *Beagle* and his experience of selectively breeding pigeons provided evidence for the large amount of variation in the characteristics of different species (checklist **1** and **4**).

Natural selection: Malthus' work contributed to Darwin's idea of a 'struggle for existence' (competition for resources). The result is the natural selection of those organisms best suited (**adapted**) to survive (checklist **3**).

Time: Lyell's work showed Darwin that the Earth is very old, giving time for the evolution of species to occur (checklist **2**).

How species evolve – the modern argument summarised

1 Because individuals vary genetically, individuals are slightly different from one another.

2 This variation in a population of individuals is the raw material on which natural selection works, resulting in evolution.

3 Individuals with genes that express characteristics which adapt the individuals to obtain scarce resources are more likely to survive than other less well adapted individuals.

4 The best adapted individuals are more likely to survive and reproduce, and so their offspring will inherit the genes for those favourable characteristics.

5   In this way organisms accumulate genes for favourable characteristics and change through time; that is, they evolve over many generations.

6   If the environment in which individuals are living changes, then genes for different characteristics might favour survival. Individuals with these characteristics will survive to reproduce and so evolution continues from generation to generation.

> It took Darwin nearly 30 years to develop a theory of evolution through natural selection. The ideas were a revolution in scientific thinking.

Evolution in action

Evolution is still happening. Maintaining the balance between the pale and the dark forms of the peppered moth *Biston betularia* is an example. The diagram below shows what happens.

The fossil record

Fossils are the remains of dead organisms, or impressions made by them. Fossils are usually preserved in sedimentary rocks which are formed layer on layer by the deposition of mud, sand and silt over millions of years. Providing the layers are undisturbed, then the more recent the layer, the nearer it is to the Earth's surface.

As a result, the fossils in each rock layer are a record of life on Earth at the time when the layer was formed.

As a result, a sequence of layers each with its fossils traces the history of life on Earth.

Extinction

Species may die out (become **extinct**) because of the harmful effects of human activities on the environment. Natural extinction also happens over longer periods of time. It makes room for new species to evolve and replace the previous ones. Naturally occurring extinctions are caused by

*   competition between species
*   changes in the environment.

The mass extinction of whole groups of organisms have occurred at intervals throughout the history of life on Earth. Extinction of the dinosaurs and many other species of reptile about 70 million years ago is a well known example. Their extinction made way for mammals and birds to fill the vacant spaces in the environment.

> That's why you and I are here!

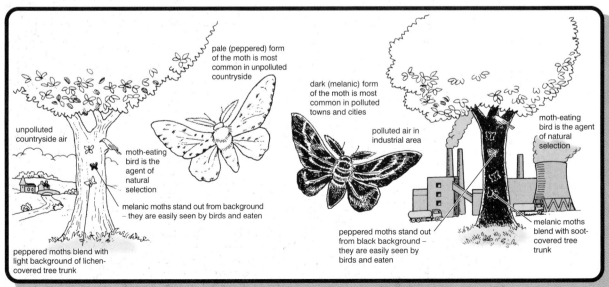

Different forms of *Biston betularia* adapt the moth to survive in different environments

round-up

How much have you improved?
Work out your improvement index on page 140.

1 Match each structure in column **A** with its correct description in column **B**.

A structures	B descriptions
seed	structure to which pollen grains attach
ovule	produces a sugar solution
fruit	contains the egg nucleus
stigma	a fertilised ovule
nectary	develops from the ovary after fertilisation [5]

2 What are the advantages to growers of reproducing crops asexually? [3]

3 Name the food stored in the organs of asexual reproduction of plants. [1]

4 Briefly explain why the production of clones depends on the process of mitosis. [5]

5 Match each term in column **A** with its correct description in column **B**.

A terms	B descriptions
allele	the processes by which a single characteristic passes from parents to offspring
pure breeding	offspring of the offspring of the parental generation
second filial generation	characteristics that appear unchanged from generation to generation
monohybrid inheritance	one of a pair of genes that control a particular characteristic [4]

6 In a population of 300 goldfish, variations in two characteristics were measured and the results displayed as charts. Chart A shows variation in the length of the fish; chart B shows variation in their colour.

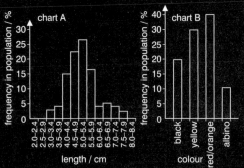

a) Which chart shows
  (i) continuous variation
  (ii) discontinuous variation?
  (iii) Briefly give reasons for your answers. [6]

b) Using chart B, calculate the percentage of yellow goldfish in the population. [1]

c) Albino goldfish are relatively rare. Give a possible genetic explanation for the occurrence of albino goldfish. [1]

7 a) Look at the diagram opposite. Briefly explain why the population densities of pale peppered moths and dark peppered moths are different in the countryside from in industrial areas. [8]

b) Why is the moth-eating bird called an agent of natural selection? [2]

8 Briefly explain why genes for characteristics that favour the survival of individuals tend to accumulate from generation to generation. [4]

9 Outline the contributions of the ideas of Charles Lyell and Thomas Malthus to Darwin's development of a theory of evolution through natural selection. [5]

Well done if you've improved. Don't worry if you haven't. Take a break and try again.

Biotechnology

preview

At the end of this section you will:

- **know that the processes of biotechnology have a long history in the production of bread and alcoholic drinks**
- **understand that the techniques of genetic engineering manipulate genes to human advantage**
- **realise that genetic engineering has transformed biotechnology into a rapidly expanding industry which provides food, medicines and a range of industrial chemicals.**

How much do you already know?
Work out your score on pages 140–1.

Test yourself

1 Briefly explain why the production of wine depends on the incomplete breakdown of glucose molecules during anaerobic respiration. [3]

2 Distinguish between the following.
a) restriction enzyme and ligase (splicing enzyme) [7]
b) biotechnology and genetic engineering [5]
c) batch culture and continuous culture [7]

3 Plants are a store of energy. Briefly explain how biotechnology converts the stored energy in plants into fuel. [8]

4 Many types of washing powder contain enzymes. Which types of enzyme are best for washing food-stained clothing? [6]

5 Nitrogen-fixing bacteria, which convert nitrogen in the atmosphere into nitrates, live in swellings on the roots of leguminous plants. Cereal plants do not contain nitrogen-fixing bacteria. How do you think food production and the environment would benefit from biotechnology which manipulates nitrogen-fixing bacteria to live in the roots of cereal plants? [9]

6 a) What is single cell protein? [2]
 b) Single cell protein is produced from bacteria grown on methanol in a fermenter at 40°C.
   (i) Explain the importance of keeping the fermenter at a constant temperature of 40°C. [4]
   (ii) State two forms in which single cell protein is sold. [2]
   (iii) State three advantages of using bacteria to produce protein food. [4]
   (iv) Briefly explain the importance of methanol in the process. [3]

7 Why do you think people might be reluctant to eat food made from microorganisms? [1]

8.1 Introducing biotechnology

Fact file

★ The word **biotechnology** describes the way we use plant cells, animal cells and microorganisms to produce substances that are useful to us.

Using biotechnology

The history of biotechnology demonstrates the importance of this area of biology.

The traditional: for thousands of years humans have exploited organisms to make food, using
- **yeast** to make wine, beer and bread
- **moulds** to make cheese
- **bacteria** to make yogurt and vinegar.

The diagram opposite traces the processes in the production of wine and bread.

Yeast cells use **anaerobic respiration** (see page 73) to convert glucose into **ethanol** ('alcohol' in wines and beers) and **carbon dioxide** (the gas that makes bread rise). The reaction is called **fermentation**. Biotechnology exploits a range of fermentation reactions to produce different substances.

The new: in the 1970s scientists developed the techniques of **genetic engineering,** which introduced the modern era of biotechnology. New methods of manipulating genes became possible because of the discovery of different enzymes in bacteria.

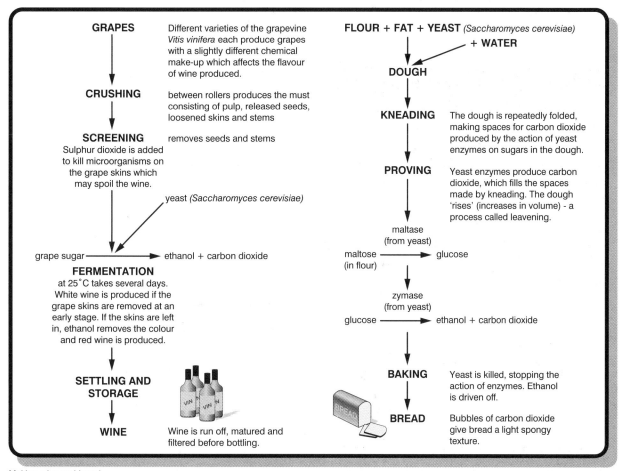

GRAPES — Different varieties of the grapevine *Vitis vinifera* each produce grapes with a slightly different chemical make-up which affects the flavour of wine produced.

CRUSHING — between rollers produces the must consisting of pulp, released seeds, loosened skins and stems

SCREENING — removes seeds and stems

Sulphur dioxide is added to kill microorganisms on the grape skins which may spoil the wine.

yeast (*Saccharomyces cerevisiae*)

grape sugar ——→ ethanol + carbon dioxide

FERMENTATION
at 25°C takes several days. White wine is produced if the grape skins are removed at an early stage. If the skins are left in, ethanol removes the colour and red wine is produced.

SETTLING AND STORAGE

WINE — Wine is run off, matured and filtered before bottling.

FLOUR + FAT + YEAST (*Saccharomyces cerevisiae*) + WATER

DOUGH

KNEADING — The dough is repeatedly folded, making spaces for carbon dioxide produced by the action of yeast enzymes on sugars in the dough.

PROVING — Yeast enzymes produce carbon dioxide, which fills the spaces made by kneading. The dough 'rises' (increases in volume) - a process called leavening.

maltase (from yeast)

maltose (in flour) ——→ glucose

zymase (from yeast)

glucose ——→ ethanol + carbon dioxide

BAKING — Yeast is killed, stopping the action of enzymes. Ethanol is driven off.

BREAD — Bubbles of carbon dioxide give bread a light spongy texture.

Making wine and bread

★ **Restriction enzymes** cut DNA into pieces, making it possible to isolate specific genes.

★ **Ligase** (splicing enzyme) allows desirable genes to be inserted into the genetic material of host cells.

Using genetic engineering we can create organisms with specific genetic characteristics, such that they produce substances that we need and want. The microorganisms are cultured in a solution containing all the substances they require for rapid growth and multiplication inside huge containers called **fermenters**. In this way, medicines, foods and industrial chemicals can be made on an industrial scale. The diagram overleaf shows how genetically engineered insulin is made.

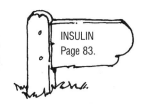
INSULIN Page 83.

Remember that the products of biotechnology come from the action of **genes** producing useful substances.

Fact file

★ **Batch culture** produces batches of product in a fermenter. The fermenter is then emptied of the product and the nutrient solution. The fermenter is sterilised with super-heated steam ready for the next batch.

★ **Continuous culture** produces substances as an ongoing process. The product is drawn off the fermenter and nutrients are replaced as they are used.

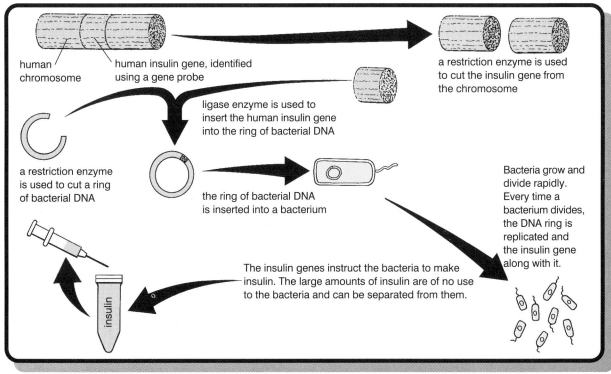

human chromosome

human insulin gene, identified using a gene probe

a restriction enzyme is used to cut the insulin gene from the chromosome

ligase enzyme is used to insert the human insulin gene into the ring of bacterial DNA

a restriction enzyme is used to cut a ring of bacterial DNA

the ring of bacterial DNA is inserted into a bacterium

Bacteria grow and divide rapidly. Every time a bacterium divides, the DNA ring is replicated and the insulin gene along with it.

The insulin genes instruct the bacteria to make insulin. The large amounts of insulin are of no use to the bacteria and can be separated from them.

insulin

Making genetically engineered insulin

8.2 Making use of biotechnology

preview

At the end of this section you will:

- **know that enzymes are useful industrial catalysts**
- **understand that plant material is a store of energy which can be converted into fuel**
- **be able to list the different applications of biotechnology on the farm**
- **understand the significance of monoclonal antibodies**
- **realise the potential of gene therapy for curing inherited diseases.**

Making the link

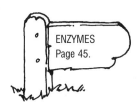

GENES
Page 116.

Modern biotechnology is branching out in new and exciting ways. Central to success is our understanding that the products of biotechnology are the result of the action of **genes**.

Enzymes

Enzymes are useful **industrial catalysts** for the following reasons.

ENZYMES
Page 45.

★ Only a particular reaction is catalysed by an enzyme, making it easier to collect and purify the products.

★ Enzyme activity is high at moderate temperature and pH.

★ Only small amounts of enzyme are required.

★ The enzyme is not used up in the reaction.

Most industrial enzymes come from microorganisms grown in nutrient solution inside large fermenters. The enzymes secreted into the nutrient solution are filtered off, concentrated and packaged for sale as liquids or powders.

Enzymes have a range of uses.

★ **Industrial** – food production, leather-making, brewing and washing powder manufacture.

★ **Medical** – diagnosis and treatment.

★ **Analysis** – environmental pollution and crime detection.

Immobilised enzymes

Enzymes may be bonded to different insoluble materials which support them. They are then called **immobilised enzymes**, and their advantages are that they are

- easily recovered and can be re-used
- active at temperatures that would destroy unprotected enzymes
- not diluted and therefore do not contaminate the product.

Immobilised enzymes are vital components of different types of **biosensor**.

Biofuel

Plants trap light energy to produce sugars by photosynthesis. Plant material therefore represents a store of energy

PHOTOSYNTHESIS
Pages 48–51.

which the processes of biotechnology convert into **fuels** such as ethanol. Countries that lack oil resources, such as Brazil, have developed gasohol programmes. Sugar cane grows rapidly in the warm sunny environment, and is used as a substrate which yeast ferments to produce ethanol. Most yeasts die when the concentration of ethanol is more than 15%. Sugar cane waste that has not been fermented (called **bagasse**) is burnt to provide the heat to distil off ethanol from the solution, and the gasohol fuel produced is 96% ethanol. After adjustments to carburettors and fuel pumps, car engines can run on pure ethanol or an ethanol–petrol mixture. The sequence runs:

On the farm

Nearly 6000 million people populate the world. Feeding everybody is difficult, but biotechnology is helping to solve some of the problems. Developments include

- genetically engineering crops to grow in places where at present there is little chance of success
- altering nitrogen-fixing bacteria so that they can live in the roots of cereal crops (see nitrogen cycle on page 132)
- engineering bacteria to produce insecticides, and spraying the bacteria onto crops where they are taken up by the plants

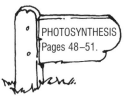
INSECTICIDES
Pages 29–30.

- producing plants resistant to disease
- developing livestock to produce more and better quality meat and milk.

Soon crops will be able to tolerate cold, flourish in drought conditions and resist insects and disease – thanks to biotechnology.

Monoclonal antibodies

Antibodies defend the body from attack by pathogens. However, it is not possible to separate out different antibodies into pure samples to fight specific diseases. White blood cells which produce antibodies are very difficult to grow outside the body. However, cancer cells are not. Fusing white blood cells that produce the desired antibody with a certain type of cancer cell results in cells called **hybridomas** which do grow outside the body. The hybridomas produce pure samples of antibodies which are called **monoclonal antibodies**.

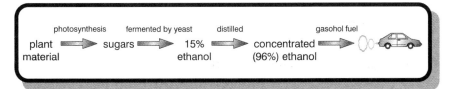

| photosynthesis | fermented by yeast | distilled | gasohol fuel |
| plant material | sugars | 15% ethanol | concentrated (96%) ethanol | |

Monoclonal antibodies have a wide range of uses, such as

- diagnosis of diseases
- detection of pregnancy
- inactivation of poisons
- tissue matching to reduce the risk of rejection of transplanted tissues
- possible treatment of cancer.

TRANSPLANTS Pages 102–3.

Gene therapy

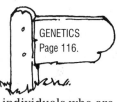

GENETICS Page 116.

We all carry a few faulty alleles. Most of them are recessive, so their harmful effects are masked by their dominant partners. However, individuals who are homozygous for recessive faulty alleles or who are heterozygous for dominant faulty alleles show symptoms of disease.

Gene therapy aims to replace the faulty alleles with normal ones. It is difficult to produce long-term cures for genetic diseases, although research is making progress. For example, **cystic fibrosis** is a genetic disease caused by a faulty recessive allele (see page 116). Healthy copies of the allele are engineered into tiny fat droplets called **liposomes**. These are carried as an aerosol spray deep into the lungs in an attempt to replace the faulty alleles in the cells of lung tissue with healthy ones. The cells seem to take up the liposomes with the healthy alleles, bringing some relief (albeit temporary) to sufferers of cystic fibrosis. Research continues to make the benefits long term.

8.3 Eating microorganisms

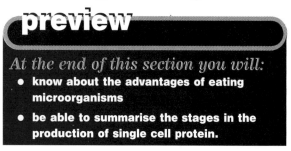

preview

At the end of this section you will:
- **know about the advantages of eating microorganisms**
- **be able to summarise the stages in the production of single cell protein.**

Making the link

How can we produce enough food to feed the world's growing population? Intensive farming and applying biotechnology to farming are options (see Sections 2.6 and 8.2). Eating organisms produced by biotechnology is another alternative.

Advantages of eating microorganisms

The problems of feeding the world's population requires imaginative solutions. Eating microorganisms produced by biotechnology is an option.

★ Microorganisms double their mass within hours. Plants and animals take weeks.

★ Microbial mass is at least 40% protein.

★ Microorganisms have a high vitamin and mineral content.

High protein food produced from microorganisms is called **single cell protein** (**SCP**).

Producing SCP

Different nutrients, such as glucose syrup, waste from papermaking and fruit pulp, are used to grow SCP microorganisms in huge fermenters which are run continuously for months at a time. Nutrients are replaced as they are used up, and temperature and pH are carefully controlled.

CONTINUOUS CULTURE Page 125.

Microorganisms are harvested at regular intervals and processed into SCP. 'Quorn', made from the mould *Fusarium graminearum*, is an example. The food is called **mycoprotein** and, unlike meat, it is high in fibre and free of cholesterol. Quorn is made into soups, biscuits and drinks as well as substituting for different meats.

round-up

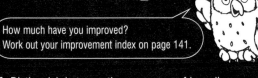

How much have you improved?
Work out your improvement index on page 141.

1 Distinguish between the processes of kneading, proving and baking in the making of bread. [6]

2 Below is a list of the processes which start with identifying the human insulin gene and result in the production of genetically engineered human insulin. Write the letters in the correct order.

A The human insulin gene is identified.

B Bacteria genetically engineered with the human insulin gene grow and divide rapidly.

C Restriction enzyme cuts open a ring of bacterial DNA.

D Large amounts of insulin are separated from the nutrient solution in which the genetically engineered bacteria are growing.

E The ring of genetically engineered bacterial DNA is inserted into a bacterium.

F Restriction enzyme cuts the human insulin gene from the chromosome.

G Ligase is used to insert the human insulin gene into a ring of bacterial DNA.

H Human insulin is purified and packed. [6]

3 What are the advantages to diabetics of using insulin produced by bacteria into which the human insulin gene has been inserted? [4]

4 Describe how monoclonal antibodies could be used to treat cancer. [4]

5 Briefly explain the principles behind treating genetic diseases by gene therapy. [2]

6 How is biotechnology helping to feed the world's growing human population? [5]

7 What is an immobilised enzyme? [3]

8 People might be reluctant to eat SCP made from microorganisms. How do you think SCP might be made more acceptable as food? [4]

9 What contribution do you think that SCP production could make to helping feed the world's growing population? [7]

Well done if you've improved. Don't worry if you haven't. Take a break and try again.

… THAT'S IT FOLKS!

Appendix: Mind Map responses and co-ordination in plants and humans

Notice that the four sections of the Mind Map correspond to Sections 4.3, 5.6, 5.7 and 5.8. The sections tell you about responses and co-ordination in plants and humans. The Mind Map reviews the whole subject, allowing you to revise

- structures
- processes
- links between ideas.

Tracking each of the sections on the Mind Map will allow you to summarise your knowledge and understanding of responses and co-ordination in plants and humans.

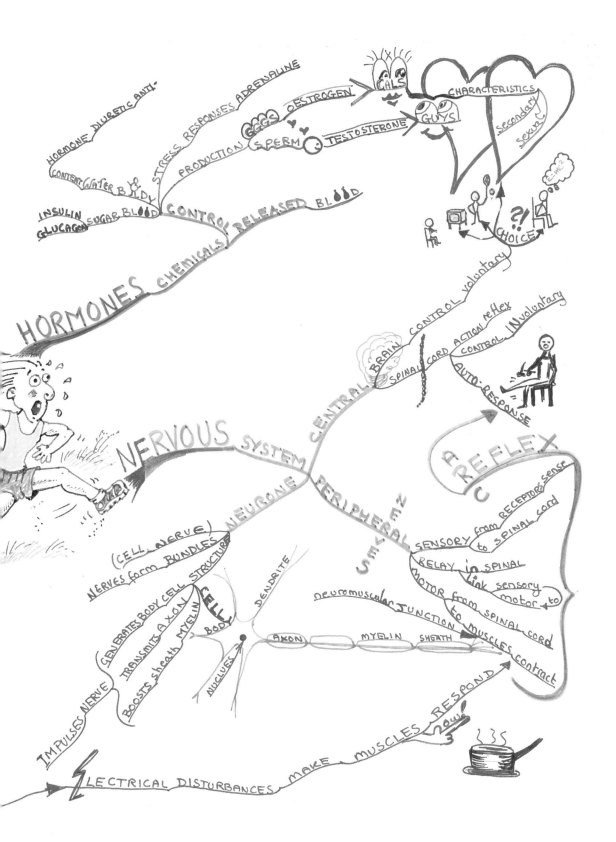

HORMONES CHEMICALS RELEASED

CONTROL

HORMONE DIURETIC ANTI-

CONTENT WATER BODY

STRESS RESPONSES ADRENALINE

PRODUCTION SPERM

OESTROGEN

TESTOSTERONE

GALS

GUYS

CHARACTERISTICS

Secondary

Sexual

INSULIN GLUCAGON

SUGAR BLOOD

BLOOD

CHOICE

?!

E=MC2

CENTRAL

BRAIN CONTROL voluntary

SPINAL CORD ACTION reflex

control INvoluntary

AUTO-RESPONSE

NERVOUS SYSTEM PERIPHERAL

NERVES

REFLEX
A
R
C

sensory from RECEPTOR sense
to SPINAL CORD

RELAY in spinal
link sensory
motor to

MOTOR from SPINAL CORD
to MUSCLES contract

NEURONE

(CELL NERVE)

NERVES form BUNDLES

GENERATES BODY CELL STRUCTURE

TRANSMITS AXON

BOOSTS sheath MYELIN

IMPULSES NERVE

neuromuscular JUNCTION

CELL BODY

DENDRITE

NUCLEUS

AXON   MYELIN   SHEATH

MUSCLES RESPOND

now!

ELECTRICAL DISTURBANCES MAKE

Appendix: Cycles of life

The amounts of nitrogen and carbon on Earth are constant. These elements cycle continually from living organisms to the air and soil and back again. The cycles below show how this happens.

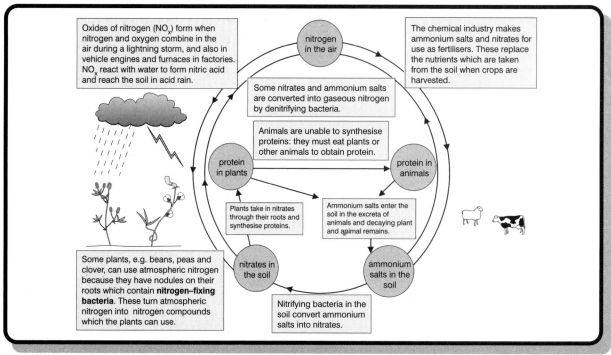

Nitrogen circulates from air to soil to living things and back again in the nitrogen cycle

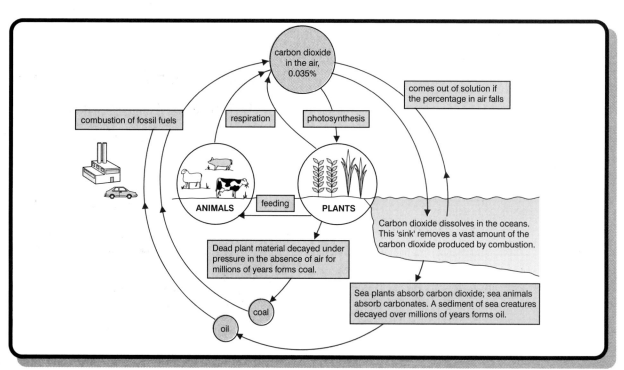

The carbon cycle shows those processes that put carbon dioxide into the air and those that remove carbon dioxide from the air

Answers

1 Test yourself (page 10)

Introducing biology

1 a) It would increase (✓).   b) It would decrease (✓).

2 a)   b)   c)

    Movement   ✓   ✗
    Respiration   ✓   ✗
    Sensitivity   ✓   ✗
    Growth   ✓   ✗
    Reproduction   ✓   ✗
    Excretion   ✓   ✗
    Nutrition   ✓   ✗   [✓ × 10]

    d) No – plants do not move from place to place (✓).

3 Annual: a plant that grows from seed to maturity and produces new seeds all within one growing season (✓). It then dies (✓). Perennial: a plant that continues to grow and produce seeds for many years (✓).

4 a) To identify different living things by name (✓).
    b) These characteristics vary too much (✗) even between members of the same group of organisms (✗) to be reliable indicators for identification (✓).

5 Soil: is damp (✓); shields organisms from ultraviolet light (✗); maintains a relatively stable temperature compared with air (✗); contains food (✓).

Your score: 14 out of 24

1 Round-up (page 15)

Introducing biology

1 a) It would boil away (✓).
    b) It would freeze and form ice (✓).

2 a) Oxygen (✓)
    b) Carbon dioxide (✓)

3 a) Respiration releases energy from food (✓). Gaseous exchange takes in oxygen needed for respiration (✓) and removes carbon dioxide produced by respiration (✓).
    b) Excretion removes the waste substances produced by metabolism (✓). Defecation removes the undigested remains of food (✓).

4 The answer should include the idea that although cars move (✓), need fuel (= nutrition) (✓), burn fuel (= respiration) (✓) and produce waste gases (= excretion) (✓) they do not grow (✓) or reproduce (✓) and are not sensitive (✓). Cars therefore do not show all the characteristics associated with living things (✓).

5

A characteristics		B descriptions
Movement	(✓)	Changing position
Respiration	(✓)	Releasing energy from food
Sensitivity	(✓)	Responding to stimuli
Growth	(✓)	Increasing in size
Reproduction	(✓)	Producing new individuals
Excretion	(✓)	Removing waste substances produced by cells
Nutrition	(✓)	Making or obtaining food

6

A animals		B descriptions
Insect	(✓)	Six legs
Worm	(✓)	No legs
Spider	(✓)	Eight legs
Bird	(✓)	Two legs

7 The unfamiliar specimen is compared with the descriptions in the key (✓).
The descriptions are followed through (✓) until the description that matches the specimen is found (✓).
The matching description identifies the specimen (✓).

8 The system gives each living organism a name in two parts (✓). The first is the name of the genus (✓); the second is the species name (✓). The genus and species names identify the organism (✓).

9 Paired statements (✓).

Your score: ☐ out of 37

Your improvement index: $\dfrac{\boxed{\ }/24}{\boxed{\ }/37} \times 100 = \boxed{\ }$ %

2 Test yourself (page 16)

Organisms in the environment

1

A terms		B descriptions
Biosphere	(✓)	All the ecosystems of the world
Community	(✓)	All the organisms that live in a particular ecosystem
Habitat	(✓)	The place where a group of organisms lives
Population	(✓)	A group of individuals of the same species

2 a) Most animals eat more than one type of plant or other animal (✓). A food web shows the range of different foods eaten (✓).
    b) Plants produce food by photosynthesis (✓). Animals consume this food directly when they eat plants (✓) or indirectly when they eat other animals (✓) which depend on plant food (✓).

133

3 a) The pyramid of biomass takes into account differences in size (✓) of producers and consumers (✓).
  b) The energy pyramid shows the amount of food being produced (✓) and consumed (✓) in a given time (✓).

4 Improvements in food production (✓); more jobs (✓); new drugs (accept improvement in medicines/medical care) (✓); improvement in public health (✓).

5 Benefits: more food (✓), reliably produced (✓). Costs: loss of wildlife (✓), loss of habitats (✓), pollution from agrochemicals (✓). (Accept other sensible alternatives.)

Your score: ☐ out of 24

2 Round-up (page 31)

Organisms in the environment

1 Physical *or* abiotic (✓), environment (✓), living *or* biotic (✓), community (✓), habitats (✓), niches (✓).

2 a) The non-living part of an ecosystem (✓).
  b) The amount of light affects the rate of photosynthesis (✓) and therefore the amount of plant growth under the canopy layer (✓). This in turn affects the animals that depend on plants for food and shelter (✓) and so on along the food chain (✓).

3 a) 3 (✓)
  b) Water weed (✓)
  c) Water weed makes food by photosynthesis (✓).
  d) Tadpoles (✓)
  e) Tadpoles eat water weed (accept plants) (✓).
  f) Minnows (✓) and perch (✓).
  g) Minnow and perch eat tadpoles (accept meat) (✓).

4 Light is reflected from the leaf surface (✓). Light passes through the leaf (✓). Only red and blue light is absorbed by chlorophyll (✓).

5 When the different organisms in the community show an approximation (are roughly the same) in size (✓).

6 a) Saw wrack (✓).
  b) Dog whelks (✓).
  c) The biomass of dog whelks would decrease (✓). The biomass of saw wrack would increase (✓).

7 a) Intraspecific competition – competition between individuals of the same species (✓). Interspecific competition – competition between individuals of different species (✓).
  b) Adaptation – an organism is adapted (suited) to survive (✓). Survival – an organism survives (lives) because of its adaptations (✓).
  c) Camouflage – coloration that conceals organisms (✓). Warning coloration – colours that deter predators from attacking prey (✓).

8 a) When prey is scarce predator numbers fall (✓). When prey numbers build up predator numbers follow because there is more prey food (✓). Predator breeds and reproduces more slowly than prey (✓).
  b) The population numbers of each species are stable (✓). (Allow: population numbers of each species fluctuated around a mean (average) number for that species.)
  c) Numbers would increase (✓).
  d) Numbers would decline (✓) to the former level (✓).
  e) Numbers would decline (✓) because of lack of food (✓). (Allow sensible alternative suggestions, e.g. increased mortality due to disease or parasites.)

9

A terms		B descriptions
Fertiliser	(✓)	Supplies plants with nutrients
Herbicide	(✓)	Kills plants
Irrigation	(✓)	Supplies plants with water
Monoculture	(✓)	A crop grown over a large area
Weed	(✓)	An unwanted plant

Your score: ☐ out of 47

Your improvement index: $\dfrac{\boxed{}/47}{\boxed{}/24} \times 100\% = \boxed{}\%$

3 Test yourself (page 32)

Cell activity

1

A structures		B functions
Mitochondrion	(✓)	Where energy is released from the oxidation of glucose
Cell membrane	(✓)	Partially permeable to substances in solution
Chloroplast	(✓)	Where light energy is captured
Cell wall	(✓)	Fully permeable to substances in solution
Nucleus	(✓)	Contains the chromosomes

2 Because molecules of the substance are moving against a concentration gradient (✓).

3 a) A plasmolysed cell is one from which water has passed out of the vacuole, out of the cytoplasm, out of the cell membrane and cell wall into the solution outside the cell (accept water has passed out of the cell) (✓). As a result the cytoplasm pulls away from the cell wall (accept cell content disrupted) (✓) and the cell becomes limp (✓). A turgid cell is one which contains as much water as it can hold (✓).
  b) A fully permeable membrane allows most substances to pass through it (✓). A partially permeable membrane allows some substances to pass through it (✓) and stops other substances (✓).

4 A group of genetically identical cells (or organisms) (✓).

5 During replication each chromosome (and its DNA) (✓) makes an exact copy of itself (✓).

6 a) Cells die (✓). New cells (✓) which are replicas of the old cells are produced by mitosis (✓).

b) The daughter cells have the same number of chromosomes as the parent cell (✓). The chromosomes in the daughter cells are identical to those in the parent cells (✓).

7 Haploid cells receive half the diploid number of chromosomes (✓) from their parent cell (✓).
Diploid cells receive the full number of chromosomes (✓) from their parent cell (✓).

8 Cells (✓), cells (✓), tissues (✓), an organ (✓), organs (✓), an organ(✓).

9 Cellulose in plant cell walls (✓); chitin in insect exoskeletons (✓).

10 The molecules of unsaturated fats have double bonds between some carbon atoms (✓). Saturated fats have only single bonds between carbon atoms (✓).

11 A nucleotide consists of the sugar ribose (✓) or deoxyribose (✓), one of five different bases (✓) and a phosphate group (✓).

Your score: ☐ out of 39

3 Round-up (page 47)

Cell activity

1 a) Nucleus (✓), cell membrane (✓), mitochondria (✓), cytoplasm (✓).
b) Cell wall (✓), large vacuole (✓), chloroplasts (✓).

2 Water is taken into the cells (✓) by osmosis (✓). The cells become turgid (✓). The wilted plant (✓) will become upright again (✓) as its cells become turgid following watering.

3 Down (✓), faster (✓), against (✓), energy (✓), partially (✓), osmosis (✓).

4 Damaged tissues can be replaced by new cells that are identical to the parent cells (✓).

5 Similarities: replication of each chromosome into chromatids (✓); lining up of the chromosomes on the equator of the cell (✓); separation of the chromatids (✓); chromatids form the new chromosomes in daughter cells (✓); destruction and reformation of the nuclear membrane during the process of cell division (✓).
Differences: chromosomes form homologous pairs in meiosis but not in mitosis (✓); there are two divisions during meiosis but only one division during mitosis (✓); meiosis results in four daughter cells, mitosis in two daughter cells (✓).

6 Cells (✓), tissues (✓), organs (✓), organ systems (✓), organism (✓).

7

A substances		B functions
Fat	(✓)	Insulates the body
Cellulose	(✓)	A component of the plant cell wall
DNA	(✓)	Carries the genetic code
Polypeptide	(✓)	Made of about 40 amino acids
Glycogen	(✓)	A food substance stored in the liver
Protein	(✓)	Enzymes are made of this substance

8 a) 4 (✓) **b)** 4 (✓)

Your score: ☐ out of 40

Your improvement index: $\dfrac{\boxed{}/40}{\boxed{}/39} \times 100\% = \boxed{}\%$

4 Test yourself (page 48)

Green plants as organisms

1 a) Carbon dioxide (✓) and water (✓).
b) Oxygen (✓).

2

A substances		B functions
Nitrogen	(✓)	Used to make protein
Phosphorus	(✓)	Used to make cell membranes
Magnesium	(✓)	Used to make chlorophyll

3 Increase (✓), osmotic (✓), osmosis (✓), xylem (✓), active transport (✓), xylem (✓), evaporation (✓), stomata (✓).

4

A tropisms		B descriptions
Phototropism	(✓)	Growth movement in response to light
Geotropism	(✓)	Growth movement in response to gravity
Hydrotropism	(✓)	Growth movement in response to water
Thigmotropism	(✓)	Growth movement in response to touch

Your score: ☐ out of 18

4 Round-up (page 57)

Green plants as organisms

1 Palisade cells (✓), spongy mesophyll cells (✓), guard cells (✓).

2 The cells of the upper surface of the leaf do not contain chloroplasts (✓). Most light therefore reaches the palisade cells (✓) which are packed with chloroplasts (✓). Photosynthesis occurs at a maximum rate (✓).

3 Temperature (✓), light intensity (✓), supplies of carbon dioxide (✓) and water (✓). A modern greenhouse provides warmth (✓), lighting (✓), a source of carbon dioxide (✓) and water from sprinkler systems (✓).

4 Sugar (✓), sugar (✓), phloem (✓), sugar (✓), phloem (✓), active transport (✓), water (✓), phloem (✓), pressure (✓), translocation (✓), sugar (✓), pressure (✓), phloem (✓).

5 Warm (✓), windy (✓), low humidity (✓) and bright sunlight (✓).

6 The stomata close (✓). If the plant continues to lose more water than it gains then its cells lose turgor (✓) and it wilts (✓).

7

Xylem		Phloem
Dead tissue (cells)	(✓)	Living tissue (cells)
Tissue (cells) waterproofed with lignin	(✓)	Tissue (cells) not waterproofed with lignin
Transports water and minerals	(✓)	Transports sugar and other substances
Transport of materials is one way	(✓)	Transport of materials is two ways
Xylem tissue does not have companion cells	(✓)	Phloem tissue has companion cells

8 Plant hormone (✓), tip (✓), weedkiller (✓), unfertilised (✓), seedless (✓), ripens (✓).

9 a) Hypothesis: a substance produced in the shoot tip of a growing seedling (✓) controls the response of the shoot to light (✓).

b) A: the shoot will remain upright and not bend towards the source of light (✓).
Explanation: the piece of metal prevents the substance that controls the response of the shoot to light and which is produced in the shoot tip (✓) from diffusing to the region behind the shoot tip where it has its effect (✓).
B: the shoot will bend towards the source of light (✓).
Explanation: the substance that controls the response of the shoot to light and which is produced in the shoot tip (✓) is able to diffuse to the region behind the shoot tip where it has its effect (✓).

Your score: ☐ out of 54

Your improvement index: $\dfrac{\boxed{}/54}{\boxed{}/18} \times 100\% = \boxed{}\%$

5 Test yourself (page 58)

Humans as organisms

1 a) Carbohydrates (✓), fats (✓), proteins (✓).
b) Protein (✓)
c) Fat (✓)
d) Minerals (✓) and vitamins (✓).

2

A terms		B descriptions
Ingestion	(✓)	Food is taken into the mouth
Digestion	(✓)	Food is broken down
Absorption	(✓)	Digested food passes into the body
Egestion	(✓)	The removal of undigested food through the anus

3 a) There are two bronchi, one branching to each lung (✓). Each bronchus branches many times into small tubes called bronchioles (✓).
b) A person has two lungs (✓). Within each lung, bronchioles subdivide into even smaller tubes which end in clusters of small sacs called alveoli (✓).

c) During aerobic respiration, cells use oxygen to oxidise digested food substances (accept glucose) (✓), releasing energy (✓). During anaerobic respiration, cells break down digested food substances (accept glucose) without oxygen (✓). Less energy is released during anaerobic respiration than during aerobic respiration (✓).
d) Breathing takes in (inhales) (✓) and expels (exhales) (✓) air. Gaseous exchange occurs across the surfaces of the alveoli (✓).

4 The right ventricle pumps blood into the pulmonary artery (✓) on its way to the lungs (✓); the left ventricle pumps blood into the aorta (✓) which takes it around the rest of the body (✓).

5

A components		B descriptions
Plasma	(✓)	Contains dissolved food substances
Red blood cells	(✓)	Contain haemoglobin
White blood cells	(✓)	Produce antibodies
Platelets	(✓)	Promote the formation of blood clots

6 Receptor (✓), sensory neurone (✓), relay neurone (✓), motor neurone (✓), effector.

7 a) The eardrum vibrates (✓) in response to sound waves (✓).
b) The bones pass vibrations through the middle ear (✓) and also amplify them (✓).
c) The pinna funnels sound waves down the ear canal (✓) to the eardrum (✓).
d) The hair cells are stimulated by the vibrations of the basilar membrane (✓). They fire off nerve impulses to the brain along the auditory nerve (✓).

8 Hormones are chemical substances (✓) which circulate in the blood (✓).

9 Insulin decreases the level of glucose in the blood (✓). Glucagon increases the level of glucose in the blood (✓).

10 Glomerulus (✓), Bowman's capsule (✓), tubule (✓), collecting duct (✓), ureter (✓), bladder (✓), urethra (✓).

11 The large pointed canines (✓) allow the dog to grip the food firmly (✓). The carnassial teeth (✓) in the upper and lower jaws cut the food (✓).

12 Beating cilia covering the gills (✓) draw a current of water containing microscopic organisms (✓) between the shells (✓). The microscopic organisms are trapped (✓) in the mucus covering the gills (✓). The mucus and food are then drawn into the mouth (✓).

13

A skeletons		B descriptions
Endoskeleton	(✓)	The skeleton lies inside the body
Exoskeleton	(✓)	The skeleton surrounds the body
Hydrostatic skeleton	(✓)	The skeleton is a body space filled with fluid

Your score: ☐ out of 66

5 Round-up (page 95)

Humans as organisms

1

A nutrients		B test results
Starch	(✓)	Produces a blue/black colour when mixed with a few drops of iodine solution
Glucose	(✓)	Produces an orange colour when heated with Benedict's solution
Fat	(✓)	Forms a milky emulsion when mixed with warm dilute ethanol
Protein	(✓)	Produces a violet/purple colour when mixed with dilute sodium hydroxide and a few drops of copper sulphate solution

2

A enzymes		B roles
Amylase	(✓)	Digests starch to maltose
Pepsin	(✓)	Digests protein to polypeptides
Lipase	(✓)	Digests fat to fatty acids and glycerol
Maltase	(✓)	Digests maltose to glucose

3 Oxygen (✓), carbon dioxide (✓), alveoli (✓), surface area (✓), exchange (✓), thin (✓), moist (✓), inhalation (✓), exhalation (✓).

4 a) Oxygenated blood contains a lot of oxyhaemoglobin (✓). It is bright red (✓). Deoxygenated blood contains little oxyhaemoglobin (✓). It is deep red-purple (✓).

b) Antibodies are proteins (✓) produced by lymphocytes (accept white blood cells) (✓) in response to antigens (✓) which are materials 'foreign' to (accept not recognised by) the body (✓). Antibodies destroy antigens (✓).

c) HIV is the abbreviation for human immunodeficiency virus (✓) which causes the diseases (✓) that characterise AIDS (✓).

d) Haemoglobin is the protein (✓) in red blood cells (✓) that absorbs oxygen (✓). Haemophilia is a genetic disease (✓) characterised by the slow clotting time of blood (✓).

e) A thrombus is a clot (✓) that causes a thrombosis (blockage) (✓) in a blood vessel (✓).

5

A parts of cell		B descriptions
Axon	(✓)	Transmits nerve impulses from the cell body
Dendrite	(✓)	Carries nerve impulses to the cell body
Sheath	(✓)	Boosts the transmission of nerve impulses
Nerve impulse	(✓)	Minute electrical disturbances

6 a) The blind spot is the region of the retina insensitive to light (✓). The fovea is the most sensitive region of the retina, where cone cells are most dense (✓).

b) The pupil is the central hole formed by the iris (✓). The iris is the coloured ring of muscle that controls the amount of light entering the eye (✓).

c) The cornea bends light (✓) and helps to focus light onto the retina (✓).

7 Endocrine glands are ductless glands (✓) which release hormones directly into the blood (✓).

8 Antidiuretic hormone promotes reabsorbtion of water into the body (✓) by making the collecting duct of the nephron more permeable to water (✓).

9 a) Raised hairs trap a layer of air (✓) which insulates the body in cold weather (✓). Air is a poor conductor of heat (✓).

b) Sweat cools the body because it carries heat energy away from the body (✓) as it evaporates (✓).

10 The extra length of the tadpole's digestive system means that cellulose-digesting microorganisms (✓) have more time (✓) to digest plant material (✓). The shorter adult digestive system suggests that microorganisms are not an important component of the adult's digestive processes (✓).

11 Calcium (✓), keratin (✓), hardest (✓), sugar (✓), acid (✓), softens (✓), dentist (✓).

Your score: ☐ out of 67

Your improvement index: $\dfrac{\boxed{}/67}{\boxed{}/66} \times 100\% = \boxed{}\%$

6 Test yourself (page 98)

Health and disease

1 Non-infectious diseases develop because the body is not working properly (✓); two from, for example, cancer, arthritis, scurvy, schizophrenia, haemophilia (allow sensible alternatives) (✓✓).
Infectious diseases are caused by organisms (allow pathogens) (✓) which can be passed from one person to another (✓); two from, for example, 'flu, chickenpox, mumps, AIDS, tuberculosis (allow sensible alternatives) (✓✓).

2

A body structures		B roles
Tear gland	(✓)	Produces the enzyme lysozyme which destroys bacteria
Glands in the stomach wall	(✓)	Produce hydrochloric acid which kills bacteria
Skin	(✓)	Produces sebum which kills bacteria and fungi
Cilia lining the upper respiratory tract	(✓)	Sweep away mucus containing trapped microorganisms and particles
Blood	(✓)	White cells produce antibodies which destroy antigens

3 The body takes a few days to produce antibodies against a first-time infection (✓). The individual therefore develops symptoms of disease (✓). If the same pathogen infects again, the body reacts more quickly (✓) producing antibodies which destroy the pathogen before symptoms develop (✓). The rapid response on reinfection is due to immunological memory (✓).

4 a) Donor – the person from whom organs or tissues are taken for transplantation (✓).
Recipient – the person who receives organs or tissues from the donor (✓).

b) Human lymphocyte antigens are carried on cell membranes (✓) except the membranes of red blood cells (✓). Red blood cell antigens are called antigen A and antigen B (✓). They determine which blood group a person belongs to (✓).

c) Immunosuppressive drugs prevent an immune response (✓) between the recipient and the donor organs or tissues (✓). Antibiotic drugs destroy bacteria (✓), preventing infection (✓).

5 Any five from: sterilisation; pasteurisation; refrigeration; freezing; drying; irradiation; ohmic heating; chemical preservatives; pickling; jam-making; smoking (✓✓✓✓).

6 Household rubbish may be incinerated (✓), dumped into holes in the ground (landfill sites) (✓) or recycled (✓).

7 Antiseptics are chemicals that stop microorganisms from multiplying (✓) and can be used to clean skin (✓). Disinfectants kill microorganisms (✓) and are used to keep surfaces free of microorganisms (✓). Aseptic procedures aim to prevent microorganisms from infecting wounds (✓).

8 The mosquito feeds on the blood (✓) of a person infected with the malaria parasite. The mosquito sucks up the parasite with the blood (✓) through its hollow mouthparts (✓). The parasite develops within the gut of the mosquito (✓) before migrating to the mosquito's salivary glands (✓). When the mosquito next feeds on another person, the malaria parasite passes down the mouthparts (✓) and enters the new person's bloodstream (✓).

Your score: ☐ out of 47

6 Round-up (page 109)

Health and disease

1 Cholera (B) (✓), AIDS (V) (✓), syphilis (B) (✓), 'flu (V) (✓), pneumonia (B) (✓).

2 B-lymphocytes produce antibodies (✓) in recognition of particular antigens (✓).
T-lymphocytes do not produce antibodies (✓). They bind with an antigen (✓).
Phagocytes engulf and destroy bacteria (✓) which have been attacked by antibodies (✓).

3

A defences		B descriptions
Mucus	(✓)	Traps particles and bacteria which are removed from the body by cilia
Lysozyme	(✓)	Destroys bacteria, preventing infection of the eye
Hydrochloric acid	(✓)	Kills bacteria on food
Antibodies	(✓)	Destroy antigens
Sebum	(✓)	A substance which kills bacteria and fungi on the skin

4 5 (✓)

5 a) Antibiotics are drugs which kill bacteria (✓). Analgesics are drugs which relieve pain (✓).

b) B-lymphocytes produce antibodies (✓) which destroy antigens (✓).
T-lymphocytes do not produce antibodies (✓) but bind directly with an antigen, destroying it (✓).

c) Lung cancer is a result of the uncontrolled division of cells in lung tissue (✓).
Emphysema is caused by the destruction of the walls of the alveoli (✓).

6 Nicotine is a poison which increases the heart rate (✓) and blood pressure (✓).
Carbon monoxide combines with haemoglobin (✓) more readily than oxygen does (✓).
Tar is a mixture of substances (✓), some of which cause cancer (accept are carcinogens) (✓).

7 a) The primary immune response occurs when an antigen first invades the body (✓). The body takes a few days to produce antibodies against the antigen (accept to mount an immune response) (✓).
The secondary immune response occurs when the same antigen invades the body again (✓). Antibody production is much more rapid than during the primary immune response (accept the body mounts a rapid immune response) (✓). The rapid response is due to memory cells (✓).

b) Lymphocytes are categories of white blood cell (✓). B-cell lymphocytes (✓) produce antibodies when challenged by antigens (✓). T-cell lymphocytes (✓) have a variety of functions (✓).
Phagocytes are a type of white blood cell (✓) which engulf bacteria (and other antigens) (✓) which have been attacked by antibodies (✓), destroying them (✓).

c) T-helper cells control the production of antibodies (✓) by B-cell lymphocytes (✓).
T-cytotoxic cells destroy virus-infected cells (✓).

8 a) Tissue typing compares the HLA antigens of donor and recipient (✓), matching them as closely as possible (✓). Immunosuppressive drugs prevent the T-cell lymphocytes (✓) of the recipient from acting against the antigens in the transplanted tissue (✓).

b) Because the HLA antigens of the donor and recipient (✓) are identical (✓).

9 a) Vaccine – contains a substance that stimulates the production of antibodies (✓) which protect the person from disease-causing microorganisms (✓).
Vaccination – the introduction of a vaccine into an individual (✓).

b) Refrigeration – food is stored at a temperature between 0°C and 5°C (✓).
Freezing – food is stored at a temperature between −18°C and −24°C (✓).

c) Activated sludge process – diffusers bubble air (✓) through primary sewage effluent (✓).
Trickling filter process – primary sewage effluent is sprayed (✓) onto a filter bed (✓).

10 Boosters maintain a person's immunity by keeping up the level of antibodies in circulation (✓).

11 The victim loses water (✓) and the body quickly dehydrates (✓).

12 a) Host – an organism infected (✓) by a parasite (✓).
Vector – an organism which transfers a parasite (✓) from host to new host (✓).

b) Bactericides are antibiotic drugs (✓) which kill bacteria (✓).
Bacteristats are antibiotic drugs (✓) which prevent bacteria from multiplying (✓).

c) Chemotherapy – treatments which use drugs (✓) to attack pathogens (✓).
Resistance – the ability of a pathogen to deactivate a drug (accept withstand the effects of a drug) (✓) which had previously been an effective treatment for the pathogen (✓).

13 Precautions to slow the development of resistance include: avoiding the use of antibiotics by practising good hygiene (✓); using antibiotics only when necessary (✓); finishing a prescribed course of antibiotics (✓); switching antibiotics (✓) to slow the development of resistance to a particular antibiotic (✓); reducing the antibiotics given to farm animals (✓).

14 Treatment with drugs (✓) which destroy the malaria parasite (*Plasmodium*) (✓); destroying the mosquito vector (✓) by draining marshes/ponds/ditches (accept sensible alternatives) (✓), spraying insecticides which destroy mosquito larvae/pupae (✓) and introducing fish which eat mosquito larvae (✓); preventing contact between mosquitoes and people (✓) using bed nets (✓) and chemical repellants (✓).

Your score: ☐ out of 93

Your improvement index: $\dfrac{\boxed{}/93}{\boxed{}/47} \times 100\% = \boxed{}\%$

7 Test yourself   (page 110)

Inheritance and evolution

1 A sperm duct (✓), B urethra (✓), C scrotal sac (accept scrotum) (✓), D = testis (✓), E = penis (✓).

2

A structures		B descriptions
Corm	(✓)	A short, swollen underground stem
Runner	(✓)	A horizontal stem running above ground
Tuber	(✓)	A swelling at the end of a rhizome
Bulb	(✓)	A large underground bud

3 a) **Bb** (✓) or **bb** (✓).

b) 50% of the children would be brown eyed (✓); 50% blue eyed (✓).

4 Acquired characteristics are those produced in the individual as a result of the influence (effects) of the environment (✓). These characteristics are not the result of genetic influence (✓) and are therefore not inherited (✓).

5 Genetic recombination (✓) as a result of sexual reproduction (✓), mutation (✓), crossing over (✓) during meiosis (✓) and the effects of the environment (✓).

Well done if you mentioned crossing over!

6 During sexual reproduction, genetic material inherited from both parents (✓) recombines in the fertilised egg (✓) producing combinations of genetic material in the offspring different from the combination in each of the parents (✓). During asexual reproduction, offspring inherit identical genetic material from one parent (✓). Mutation is the only source of variation (✓).

7 a) Ancestors are organisms that give rise to offspring, who are their descendants (✓).

b) Adaptation – an organism with a structure and way of life that best suits it to survive is said to be adapted (✓). Extinction occurs when a species dies out (✓).

c) Evolution – the change that occurs through many generations of descendants from different ancestors (✓). Natural selection – the process whereby favourable variations survive (✓) so that descendants evolve from ancestors (✓). (Allow: the mechanism of evolution (✓) through the survival of favourable variations (✓).)

8 Fossil formation occurs under the following conditions:
- the replacement of decayed organic material with a permanent alternative (✓)
- the burying of an organism in hardening mud or cooling volcanic ash (✓) followed by the formation of a cast (allow: material that takes on the shape of the original organism) (✓)
- rapid freezing of the organism following its death (✓).

Your score: ☐ out of 37

7 Round-up (page 123)

Inheritance and evolution

1

A structures		B descriptions
Seed	(✓)	A fertilised ovule
Ovule	(✓)	Contains the egg nucleus
Fruit	(✓)	Develops from the ovary after fertilisation
Stigma	(✓)	Structure to which pollen grains attach
Nectary	(✓)	Produces a sugar solution

2 Plants are healthy (✓), the same (accept uniform) (✓), and retain desirable characteristics (✓).

3 Starch (✓)

4 During mitosis, the DNA of the parent cell replicates (✓) so that daughter cells receive exact copies of the parent cell's genetic material (✓). Daughter cells divide and develop into new individuals which inherit the exact characteristics of the parent (✓). Offspring of the parent are also genetically identical to one another (✓) and are a clone (✓).

5

A terms		B descriptions
Allele	(✓)	One of a pair of genes that control a particular characteristic
Pure breeding	(✓)	Characteristics that appear unchanged from generation to generation
Second filial generation	(✓)	Offspring of the offspring of the parental generation
Monohybrid inheritance	(✓)	The processes by which a single characteristic passes from parents to offspring

6 a) (i) A (✓)
 (ii) B (✓)
 (iii) Chart A shows intermediate lengths of fish (✓) over a range of measurements (✓). Chart B shows categories of colour (✓) without any intermediate forms (✓).
 b) 90% (✓)
 c) Albino fish occur as a result of a mutation of the alleles controlling colour (✓).

7 a) In unpolluted countryside, pale peppered moths blend with the light background of (are camouflaged on) the lichen-covered tree trunk (✓). Fewer are eaten by moth-eating birds (suffer less predation) (✓) than dark peppered moths (✓) which are more conspicuous (✓). In polluted industrial areas, dark peppered moths are less conspicuous against the soot-covered tree trunks (✓). Fewer are eaten by moth-eating birds (suffer less predation) (✓) than pale peppered moths (✓) which are more conspicuous (✓).
 b) The bird eats the moths which are conspicuous (✓) and therefore not adapted to blend with their surroundings (✓).

8 Individuals with genes for characteristics that favour survival are more likely to reproduce (✓). Their offspring inherit the favourable genes (✓) and in turn are more likely to survive and reproduce (✓) so handing on the favourable genes to the next generation, and so on (✓).

9 Charles Lyell stated that the Earth was very old (✓). This suggested to Darwin that there was sufficient time for the process of evolution to occur (✓). Malthus suggested that limited resources regulated population numbers (✓) which would otherwise increase indefinitely (✓). Darwin concluded that there must be a struggle for existence (competition for limited resources) (✓).

Your score: ☐ out of 45

Your improvement index: $\dfrac{\boxed{}/45}{\boxed{}/37} \times 100 = \boxed{}$ %

8 Test yourself (page 124)

Biotechnology

1 In the absence of oxygen (✓), yeast breaks down glucose anaerobically (✓) to form ethanol and carbon dioxide (✓).

2 a) Restriction enzyme cleaves (cuts up) lengths of DNA into different fragments (✓) depending on the restriction enzyme used (✓). A particular DNA fragment corresponds to a desired gene (✓). (Accept sensible alternative explanations.) Ligase splices the desired gene from among the fragments of DNA produced by restriction enzyme (✓) into a plasmid vector (✓) which is a loop of bacterial DNA (✓) into which the desired gene is inserted (✓).
 b) Biotechnology uses microorganisms (✓) on a large scale for the production of useful substances (✓). Genetic engineering manipulates genes (✓) to create organisms (✓) with specific genetic characteristics for producing a range of useful substances (✓).
 c) Batch culture produces substances in a fermenter (✓). The fermenter is then emptied of product and nutrient solution (✓) and sterilised (✓) in preparation for the next batch (✓). Continuous culture produces substances over an extended period (✓). Product is drawn off and nutrients replaced as they are used (✓) during an ongoing process (✓).

3 Photosynthesis produces sugar which is a store of energy (✓). Yeasts are used to ferment the sugar (✓), producing ethanol (✓). When the concentration of ethanol exceeds 15% the yeasts die (✓). To concentrate the ethanol so that it is a useful fuel (✓), excess water is driven off (accept distilled off (✓) by burning sugar cane waste (accept bagasse) (✓) as a source of heat for the distillation process (✓).

4 Carbohydrases (✓) which digest carbohydrates (✓); proteases (✓) which digest protein (✓); lipases (✓) which digest fats (✓).

5 Nitrogen-fixing bacteria living in the roots of cereals would provide the plants with nitrate fertiliser (✓), increasing production (✓). The need for synthetic nitrate fertilisers would diminish, saving fuel in their production (✓), reducing the amount applied to crops (✓) and therefore reducing the amount of surplus fertiliser which runs off the land into rivers and lakes (✓). Eutrophication (accept excessive growth of algae) would be avoided (✓) and wildlife would therefore benefit (accept BOD of water would not increase) (✓). Also nitrates would not pollute drinking water supplies (✓), reducing the associated hazards to health (✓).

6 a) High protein food (✓) produced from microorganisms (✓).
  b) (i) 40 °C is the best temperature for fermentation reactions to take place (✓). Fermentation reactions quickly raise the temperature inside the fermenter (✓). Temperatures of more than 60 °C (accept high temperatures) would kill the cell culture (✓). A cooling system is necessary to maintain a temperature of around 40 °C (✓).
  (ii) Marmite (✓) and Quorn (✓) are two examples. (Accept sensible alternative suggestions.)
  (iii) Microorganisms double their mass within hours (accept very quickly) (✓) compared with weeks for plants and animals (✓).
  Microbial mass is at least 40% protein (✓).
  Microbial mass has a high vitamin and mineral content (✓).
  (iv) Methanol is a substrate (✓) which bacteria ferment (accept use as food) (✓) to produce single cell protein (✓).

7 People associate microorganisms with dirt and disease (✓).

Your score: ☐ out of 61

8 Round-up (page 129)

Biotechnology

1 Kneading – repeated folding of the dough (✓) makes spaces for carbon dioxide produced by the action of yeast enzymes on the sugar in the dough (✓).
Proving – carbon dioxide fills the spaces produced by kneading (✓).
Baking – kills yeast, stopping the action of enzymes (✓).
Ethanol produced by yeast fermenting sugars (✓) is driven off (✓).

2 A, F, C, G, E, B, D, H (✓✓✓✓✓✓).

3 Genetically engineered insulin is cheaper (✓), available in large quantities (✓) and chemically the same as human insulin (✓), preventing a possible immune response to injection of the hormone (✓).

4 If monoclonal antibodies can be made that attach themselves only to cancer cell antigens (✓), and these antibodies are attached to drugs that kill cancer cells (✓), then it should be possible to target cancer cells (✓) without affecting healthy cells (✓).

5 The faulty genes are first identified (✓) using gene probes. Treatment then aims to add normal genes to the patient's genetic make-up (accept genotype) (✓).

6 Developments include
  • genetically engineering crops to grow in places where at present there is little chance of success (✓)
  • altering nitrogen-fixing bacteria so that they can live in the roots of cereal crops (✓)
  • designing insecticides produced by bacteria and which are selective for particular insect pests (✓)
  • producing plants resistant to disease (✓)
  • developing livestock to produce more and better quality meat and milk (✓).

7 An immobolised enzyme is made by attaching the enzyme to an insoluble support (✓). This means that enzyme is not lost (✓) when the products are collected (✓).

8 Addition of colours (✓) and flavours (✓); blending with meat (✓) produces acceptable food (✓).

9 High protein food (✓) which is also high in vitamins and minerals (✓) but low in cholesterol (accept cholesterol-free) (✓) is produced by industrial processes (✓) which occupy a small area of land compared with a farm (✓). Production processes can be closely controlled (✓) compared with crops and livestock which are exposed to a variety of uncontrollable environmental factors (✓).

Your score: ☐ out of 41

Your improvement index: $\dfrac{\boxed{}/41}{\boxed{}/61} \times 100 = \boxed{}$ %

Index